101 Hits for Buskers

Book 13 ◆ Piano/Organ Edition with Guitar Chords

C000157614

Wise Publications
London/New York/Sydney

Exclusive Distributors:
Music Sales Limited
8/9 Frith Street, London W1V 5TZ, England.
Music Sales Pty Limited
120 Rothschild Avenue, Rosebery, NSW2018, Australia.

This book © Copyright 1991 by Wise Publications
Order No.AM84062
ISBN 0.7119.2578.X

Art direction by Michael Bell Design.
Cover illustration by Martin Chatterton.
Compiled by Peter Evans and Peter Lavender.
Music processed by MSS Studios & Hillmob Music Services.

Music Sales' complete catalogue lists thousands of titles and
is free from your local music shop, or direct from Music Sales Limited.
Please send a cheque/postal order for £1.50 for postage to
Music Sales Limited, 8/9 Frith Street, London W1V 5TZ.

Your Guarantee of Quality:

As publishers, we strive to produce every book to
the highest commercial standards.

All the music has been freshly engraved, and the book has
been carefully designed to minimise awkward page turns and to
make playing from it a real pleasure.

Particular care has been given to specifying acid-free,
neutral-sized paper which has not been chlorine bleached but
produced with special regard for the environment.
Throughout, the printing and binding have been planned to
ensure a sturdy, attractive publication which should give years of enjoyment.

If your copy fails to meet our high standards, please inform
us and we will gladly replace it.

1
All The Love In The World

Words & Music by Barry Gibb, Robin Gibb & Maurice Gibb.

In your eyes —— I see on-ly one.

—— Find me the place to run —— That's where I be - long. ——

There we rise —— Your glo-ry and mine.—— Your pain is

o - ver now —— I make you shine Still be - liev - ing

All the love in the world won't take me a - way from you.— My

2
A Beautiful Friendship

Words by Stanley Styne. Music by Donald Kahn.

3
All The Things You Are

Music by Jerome Kern. Words by Oscar Hammerstein II.

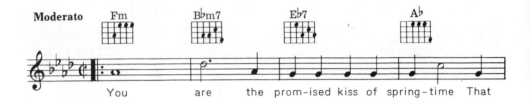

Moderato

You are the prom-ised kiss of spring-time That

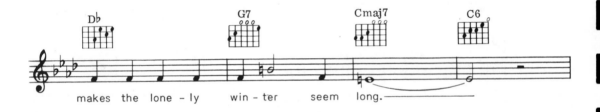

makes the lone - ly win - ter seem long.___

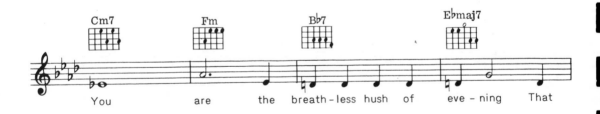

You are the breath-less hush of eve - ning That

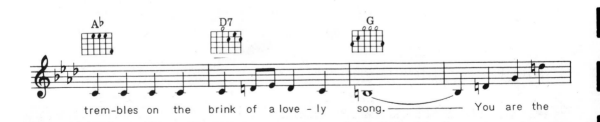

trem-bles on the brink of a love-ly song.___ You are the

an - gel glow———— that lights a star, ————————— The dear - est

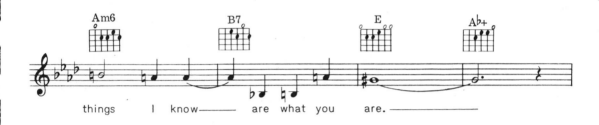

things I know———— are what you are. ————————

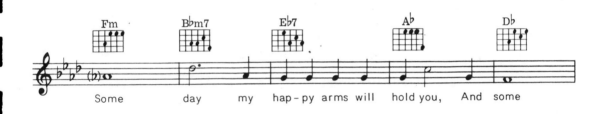

Some day my hap - py arms will hold you, And some

day I'll know that mo - ment di - vine, When all the things you

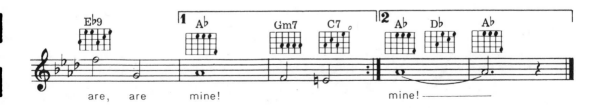

are, are mine! mine! ————————

4
A Fine Romance

Music by Jerome Kern. Words by Dorothy Fields.

5
All I Wanna Do Is Make Love To You

Words & Music by Robert John 'Mutt' Lange.

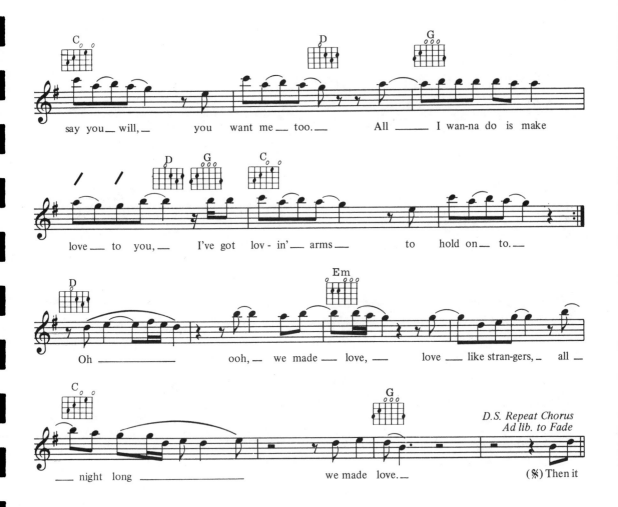

D.S. Repeat Chorus
Ad lib. to Fade

VERSE 2:
So we found this hotel, it was a place I knew well
We made magic that night, oh he did everything right
He brought the woman out of me, so many times easily
And in the morning when he woke all I left him was a note.

I told him "I am the flower you are the seed"
We walked in the garden, we planted a tree
Don't try to find me, please don't you dare
Just live in my memory, you'll always be there.

CHORUS 2:
All I wanna do is make love to you
One night of love was all we knew
All I wanna do is make love to you
I've got lovin' arms to hold on to.

D.S.
Then it happened one day, we came round the same w
You can imagine his surprise when he saw his own eye:

I said "Please, please understand
I'm in love with another man
And what he couldn't give me
Was the one little thing you can."

CHORUS 3:
All I wanna do is make love to you
One night of love was all we knew
All I want to do is make love to you
Come on say you will, you want me to.

CHORUS 4: (Repeat)
All I wanna do is make love to you
One night of love is all we knew
All I want to do is make love to you
Say you will, you want me too.

6
American Pie

Words & Music by Don McLean.

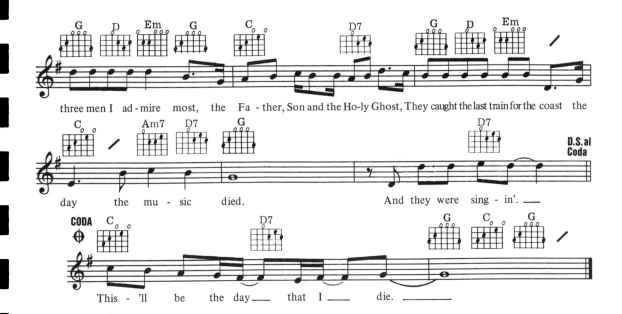

three men I ad-mire most, the Fa-ther, Son and the Ho-ly Ghost, They caught the last train for the coast the

day the mu-sic died. And they were sing-in'. ___

CODA This-'ll be the day___ that I ___ die. ___

2.
Now for ten years we've been on our own, and moss grows fat on a rollin' stone
But that's not how it used to be when the jester sang for the king and queen
In a coat he borrowed from James Dean and a voice that came from you and me
Oh and while the king was looking down, the jester stole his thorny crown
The courtroom was adjourned, no verdict was returned
And while Lenin read a book on Marx the quartet practised in the park
And we sang dirges in the dark
The day the music died
We were singin'. . . bye-bye . . . etc.

3.
Helter-skelter in the summer swelter the birds flew off with a fallout shelter
Eight miles high and fallin' fast, it landed foul on the grass
The players tried for a forward pass, with the jester on the sidelines in a cast
Now the half-time air was sweet perfume while the sergeants played a marching tune
We all got up to dance but we never got the chance
'Cause the players tried to take the field, the marching band refused to yield
Do you recall what was revealed
The day the music died
We started singin'. . . bye-bye. . . etc.

4.
And there we were all in one place, a generation lost in space
With no time left to start again
So come on, Jack be nimble, Jack be quick, Jack Flash sat on a candlestick
'Cause fire is the devil's only friend
And as I watched him on the stage my hands were clenched in fists of rage
No angel born in hell could break that Satan's spell
And as the flames climbed high into the night to light the sacrificial rite
I saw Satan laughing with delight the day the music died.
He was singin'. . . bye-bye. . . etc.

7

Bill

Music by Jerome Kern.
Words by P.G. Wodehouse & Oscar Hammerstein II.

Slowly   **VERSE**

I used to dream that I would dis - cov - er_____ the per - fect

lov - er some day. I knew I'd re - cog - nize him if

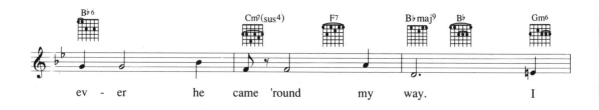

ev - er he came 'round my way. I

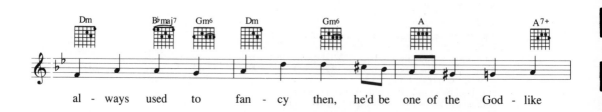

al - ways used to fan - cy then, he'd be one of the God - like

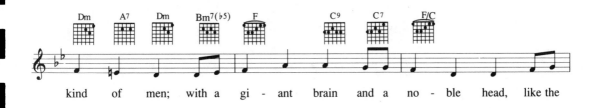

kind   of   men;   with   a   gi - ant   brain   and   a   no - ble   head,   like   the

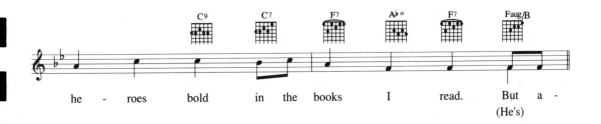

he -   roes   bold   in   the   books   I   read.   But   a -
                                                                    (He's)

CHORUS (very slowly)

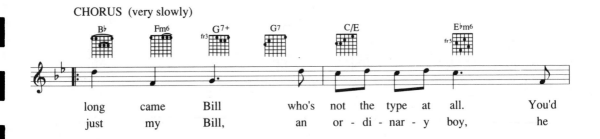

long   came   Bill   who's   not   the   type   at   all.   You'd
just   my   Bill,   an   or - di - nar - y   boy,   he

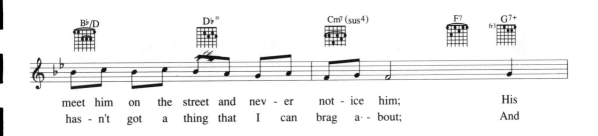

meet   him   on   the   street   and   nev - er   not - ice   him;   His
has - n't   got   a   thing   that   I   can   brag   a - bout;   And

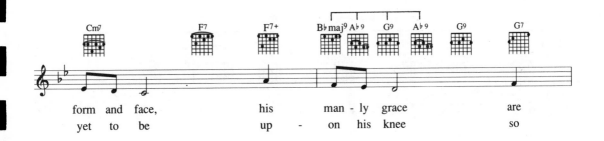

form   and   face,   his   man - ly   grace   are
yet   to   be   up -   on   his   knee   so

not the kind   that you   would find in a   sta - tue, and I
com - fy and   room - y   feels nat - ur - al   to me, and I

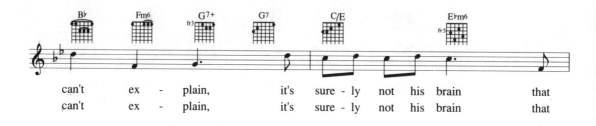

can't   ex - plain,   it's sure - ly not his brain   that
can't   ex - plain,   it's sure - ly not his brain   that

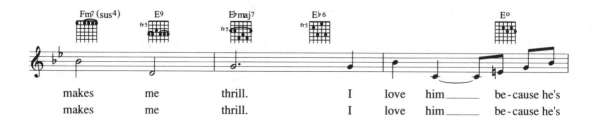

makes   me   thrill.   I love him_____ be - cause he's
makes   me   thrill.   I love him_____ be - cause he's

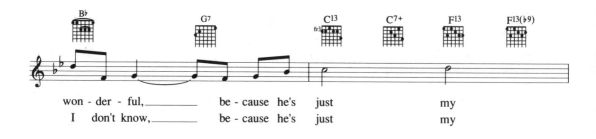

won - der - ful,_____ be - cause he's just   my
I don't know,_____ be - cause he's just   my

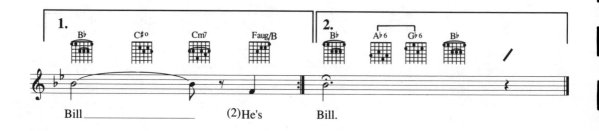

Bill_____   (2)He's   Bill.

8
Another Brick In The Wall Part II

Words & Music by Roger Waters.

9
A Picture Of You

Words & Music by Johnny Beveridge & Peter Oakman.

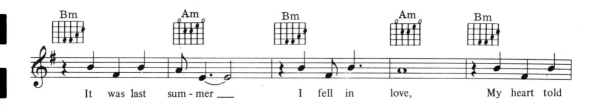

It was last sum-mer ___ I fell in love, My heart told

me what to do, ___ I saw you there on the

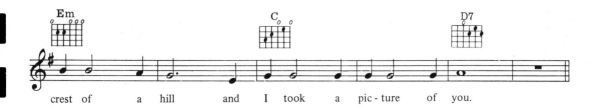

crest of a hill and I took a pic-ture of you.

Then you were gone ___ like a dream in the night, ___ With you

went my heart my love ___ and my life, ___ I did-n't know your name what could I do? ___

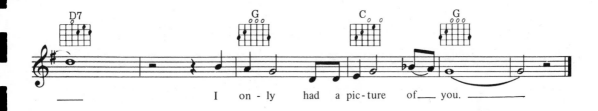

___ I on-ly had a pic-ture of ___ you. ___

10
Baby Face

Words & Music by Harry Akst & Benny Davis.

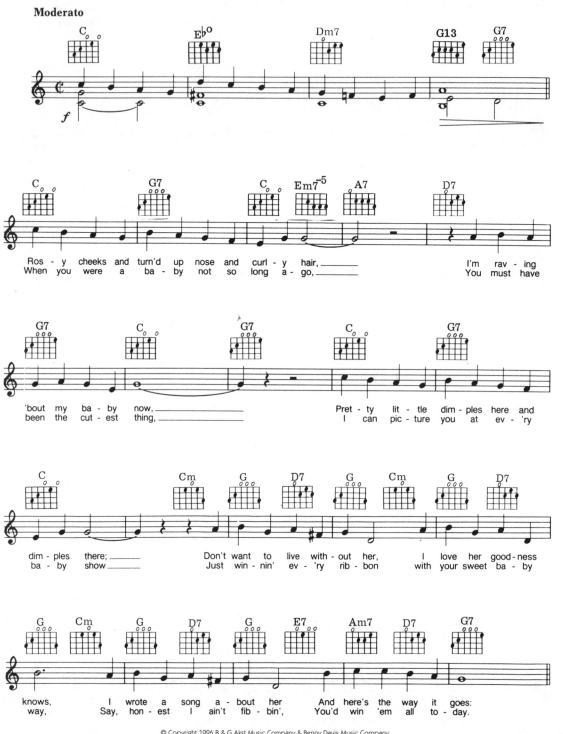

11
Bell Bottom Blues

Words & Music by Hal David & Leon Carr.

12
Birdie Song/Birdie Dance

Words & Music by Werner Thomas & Terry Rendall.
English Lyrics by Peter Foss.

Moderato

No Chord

With a lit-tle bit of this and a lit-tle bit of

that, then a lit-tle wig-gle down and up a - gain; with a lit-tle bit of

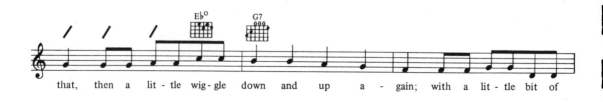

this and a lit-tle bit of that, then a lit-tle jig-gle down and up a -

gain. With a lit-tle peck for you and a lit-tle peck for me, then a lit-tle gig-gle

13
Black Velvet

Words & Music by Christopher Ward & David Tyson.

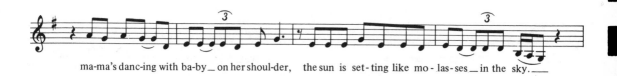

Mis-sis-sip-pi in the mid-dle of a dry spell, Jim-mie Rod-gers on the Vic-tr'-la up__ high__

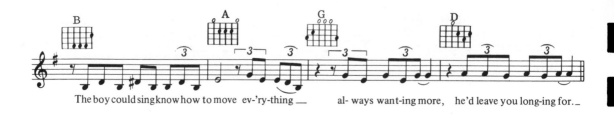

ma-ma's danc-ing with ba-by__ on her shoul-der, the sun is set-ting like mo-las-ses__ in the sky. __

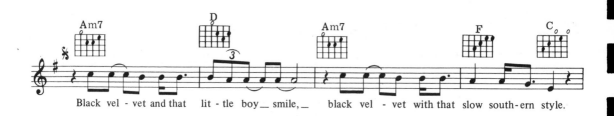

The boy could sing know how to move ev-'ry-thing __ al-ways want-ing more, he'd leave you long-ing for.__

Black vel-vet and that lit-tle boy__ smile,__ black vel-vet with that slow south-ern style.

A new re-li-gion__ that-'ll bring ya__ to your knees black vel-vet__ if you please.

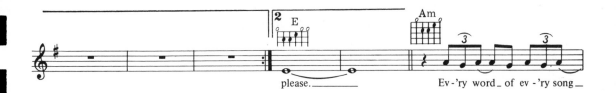

please._____

Ev-'ry word_ of ev-'ry song_

_ that he sang_was for you. _____

In a flash_ he was gone,_ it hap-pened so

soon._

What could you_ do? _____

D.S. Repeat to 2⁰ bar (8 bars)
Chorus ad lib. to Fade

VERSE 2:
Up in Memphis the music's like a heatwave
"White Lightning" bound to drive you wild
Mama's baby is in the heart of every schoolgirl
"Love me tender" leaves them crying in the aisle.

The way he moved it was so, so sweet and true
Always wanting more, he'd leave you longing for.

14
Blue Angel

Words & Music by Roy Orbison & Joe Melson.

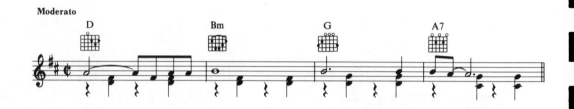

Oh, Blue An-gel, don't you cry ___ just be-cause he

said good-bye Oh, ___ Oh, ___ uh uh uh aah No, don't

cry ___ Oh, Blue An-gel, have no fear, I

brush a-way each lone-ly tear-drop Yea, yea ___

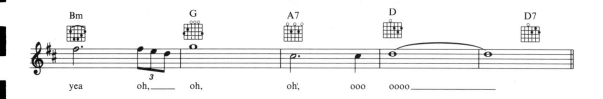

Bm   G   A7   D   D7

yea   oh,   oh,   oh,   ooo   oooo

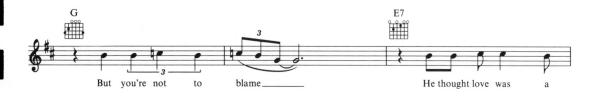

G   Em   D   Bm

Well, love's pre - cious flame_____ Just burned in vain_____

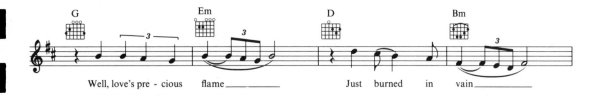

G   E7

But you're not to blame_____ He thought love was a

A7   G   D

game_____ Oh, such a shame_____ But don't you cry, don't sigh_____ I'll tell you

Em   A7

why_____ I'll nev - er say good - bye_____ Blue

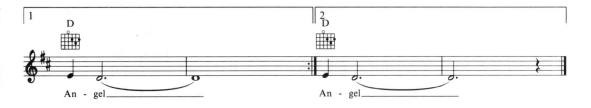

1
D

An - gel_____

2
D

An - gel_____

2. We'll have love so fine
   Magic moments divine
   If you'll just say you're mine
   I'll love you 'til the end of time
   Don't you worry your pretty head
   I'll never let you down
   I'll always be around
   Blue Angel

15
Blues Stay Away From Me

Words & Music by Wayne Raney, Henry Glover,
Alton Delmore & Rabon Delmore.

16
Castles In The Air

Words & Music by Don McLean.

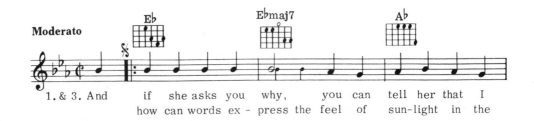

Moderato

1. & 3. And if she asks you why, you can tell her that I
how can words ex - press the feel of sun-light in the

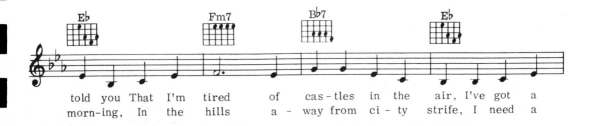

told you That I'm tired of cas-tles in the air, I've got a
morn-ing, In the hills a - way from ci - ty strife, I need a

dream I want the world to share And cas-tle walls just
coun - try wo-man for my wife, I'm ci - ty born, but I

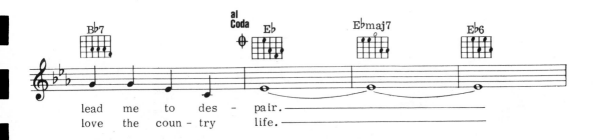

lead me to des - pair.
love the coun - try life.

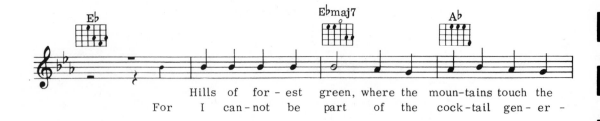

Hills of for - est green, where the moun-tains touch the
For I can-not be part of the cock-tail gen - er -

sky, A dream come true, I'll live there till I die; I'm ask-ing
- a - tion, Part-ners waltz, de - void of all ro-mance; The mu - sic

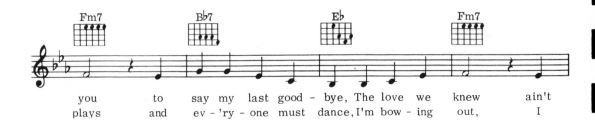

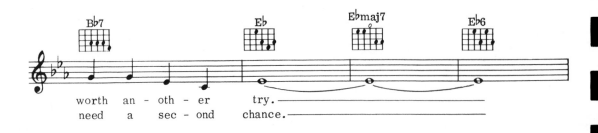

you to say my last good - bye, The love we knew ain't
plays and ev - 'ry - one must dance, I'm bow - ing out, I

worth an - oth - er try.
need a sec - ond chance.

Save me from all the trou - ble and the

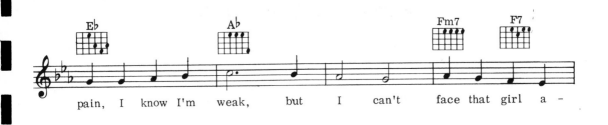

pain, I know I'm weak, but I can't face that girl a –

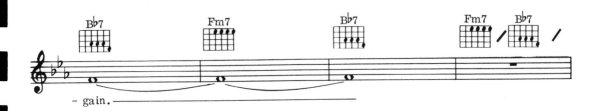

– gain. ————————

Tell her ———— the rea - son why I can't re - main, Per-haps she'll

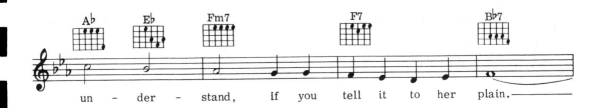

un – der – stand, if you tell it to her plain. ————

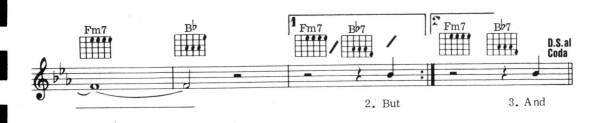

D.S. al Coda

2. But   3. And

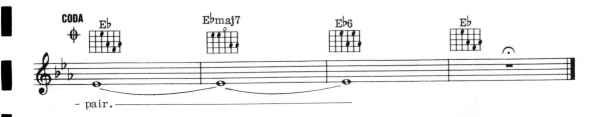

CODA

– pair. ————

17
Borne On The Wind

Words & Music by Roy Orbison & Bill Dees.

18
Breaking Hearts
(Ain't What It Used To Be)

Words & Music by Elton John & Bernie Taupin.

Moderato

They used to say that boys are
al - ways there in the
now I know what
say I blame them all for

tough as nails, in ev-'ry way he keeps his heart as guard-ed
thick of things, I al - ways had the heart of ev-'ry wo-man
lone - ly means, I used to give so lit - tle and gain
be - ing hurt aft - er all I treat-ed each and ev-'ry -

as a jail, now things have changed, I feel so
on a string, the dan - ger zone shone from my
ev - 'ry - thing, the dark - est part of ev - 'ry
- one like dirt, who wants a heart that's nev - er

old, like an - y girl could drag my heart a-cross the
eyes, it seemed like ev - 'ry inch I gained became a
day is the shadow of an - oth - er girl as she turns and walks a -
home, I face the facts and lock my-self in-to a

1.
coals. I was mile.
- way. Can't life a-lone.

2.
It's not the

19
Can't Help Lovin' Dat Man

Music by Jerome Kern. Words by Oscar Hammerstein II.

20
California Dreaming

Words & Music by John Phillips.

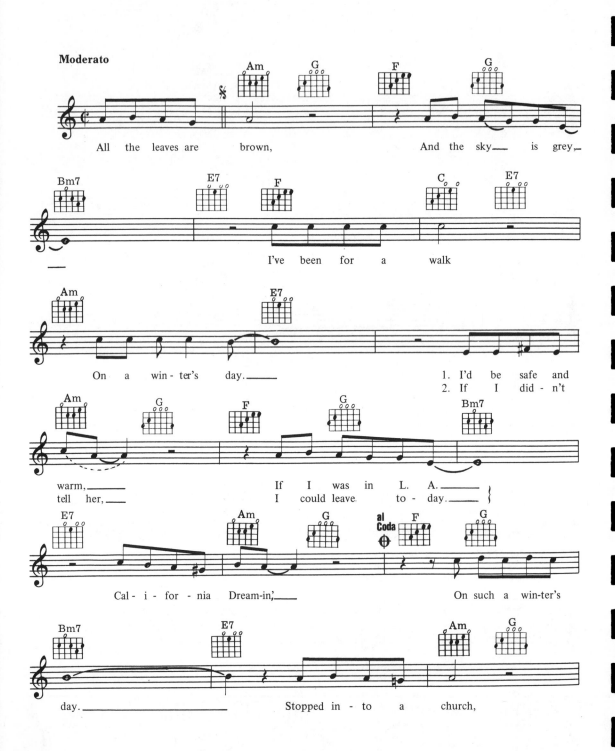

21
Cover Girl

Words & Music by Maurice Starr.

I get up in the morn - ing and I see your face, _ girl.

You're look - ing so good, ev - 'ry-thing's _

_ in place. _ Don't _

22
Danny's Song

Words & Music by Kenny Loggins.

23
Dearly Beloved

Music by Jerome Kern. Words by Johnny Mercer.

Moderato

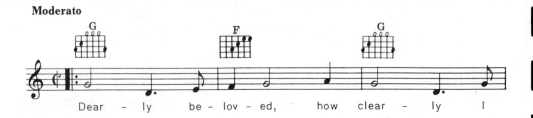

Dear – ly be – lov – ed, how clear – ly I

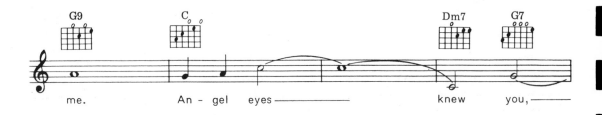

see, Some – where in Hea – ven you were fash – ioned for

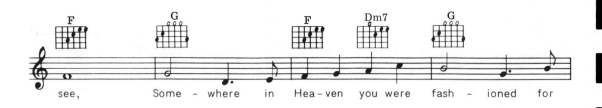

me. An – gel eyes ———— knew you, ————

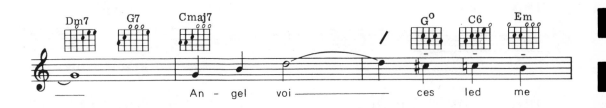

———— An – gel voi ———— ces led me

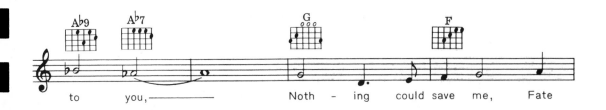

to you,————————— Noth - ing could save me, Fate

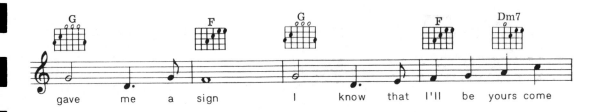

gave me a sign I know that I'll be yours come

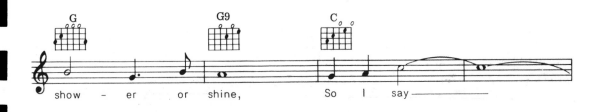

show - er or shine, So I say————————

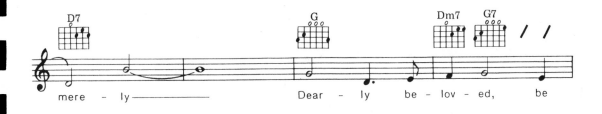

mere - ly————————— Dear - ly be - lov - ed, be

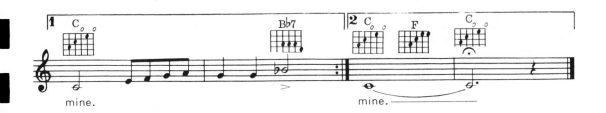

1 mine. 2 mine.—————————

24
Don't Give Up On Us

Words & Music by Tony Macauley.

Moderato

Don't give up on us ba— by Don't make the
up on us ba— by We're still worth
up on us ba— by Lord knows we've

wrong seem right, The fu-ture is-n't just one— night —
one more try, And though we put a last one — by —
come this far, Why can't we stay the way we — are —

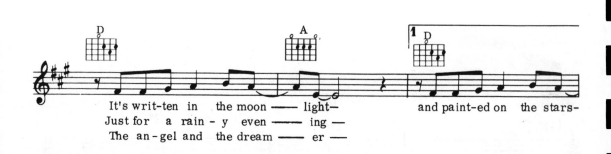

It's writ-ten in the moon —— light— and paint-ed on the stars—
Just for a rain - y even —— ing —
The an - gel and the dream —— er —

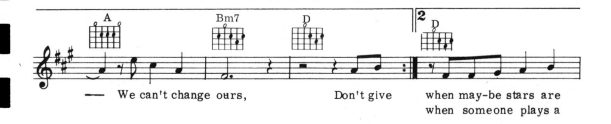

We can't change ours,   Don't give   when may-be stars are
                       when someone plays a

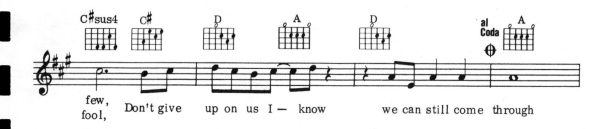

few,
fool,   Don't give   up on us I— know   we can still come through

I   near-ly lost my head last night— you've got a right to stop be-liev-

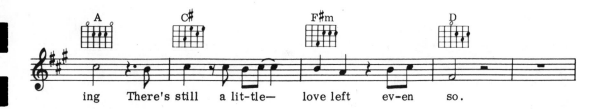

ing   There's still   a lit-tle—   love left   ev-en   so.

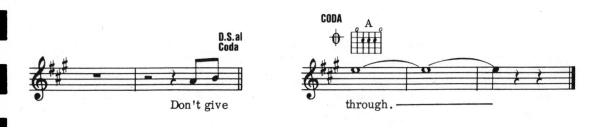

Don't give   through. ———

25
Don't Go To Strangers

Words by Redd Evans. Music by Arthur Kent & Dave Mann.

26
Don't Let The Stars Get In Your Eyes

Words & Music by Slim Willet.

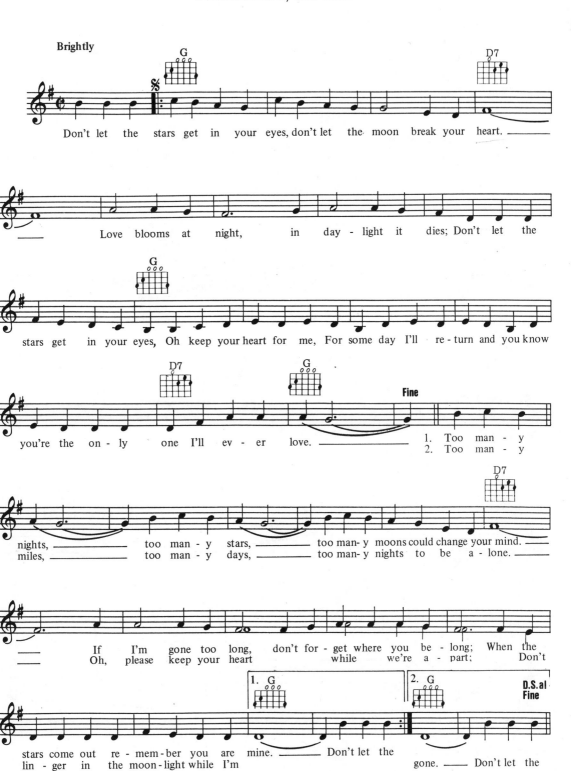

Don't let the stars get in your eyes, don't let the moon break your heart.

Love blooms at night, in day-light it dies; Don't let the

stars get in your eyes, Oh keep your heart for me, For some day I'll re-turn and you know

you're the on-ly one I'll ev-er love. _____ 1. Too man-y
                                          2. Too man-y

nights, _____ too man-y stars, _____ too man-y moons could change your mind. _____
miles, _____ too man-y days, _____ too man-y nights to be a-lone. _____

If I'm gone too long, don't for-get where you be-long; When the
Oh, please keep your heart while we're a-part; Don't

stars come out re-mem-ber you are mine. _____ Don't let the
lin-ger in the moon-light while I'm   gone. _____ Don't let the

27
Early Autumn

Words by Johnny Mercer.
Music by Ralph Burns & Woody Herman.

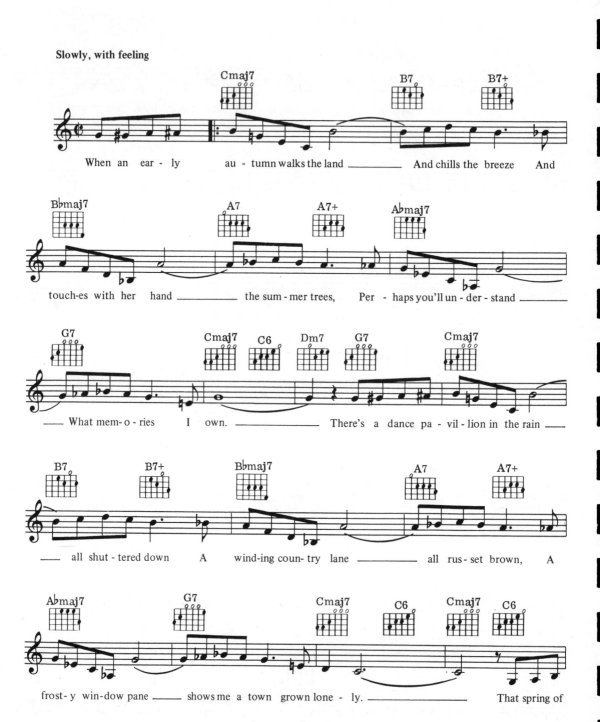

28
Falling

Words & Music by Roy Orbison.

29
Downtown Train

Words & Music by Tom Waits.

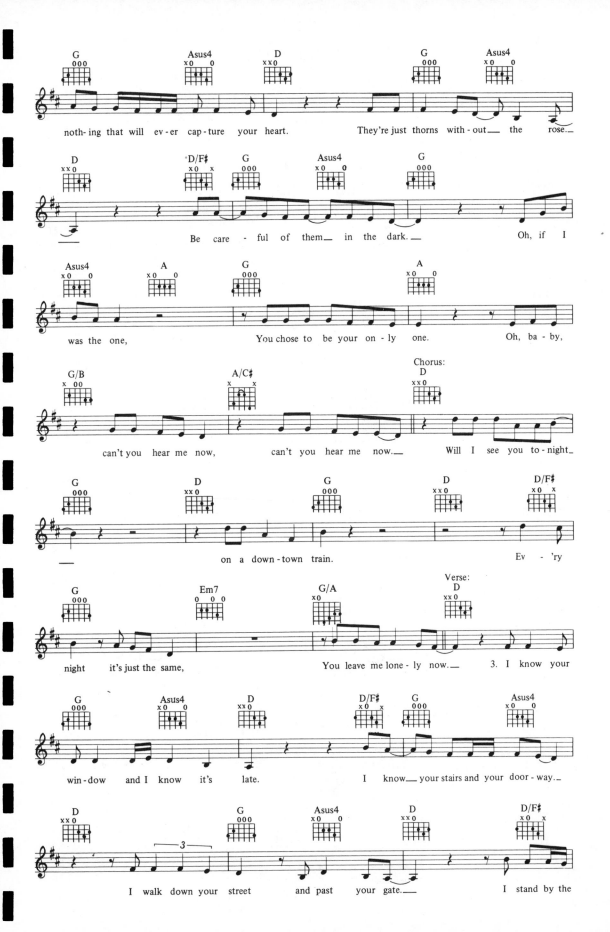

30
The Finger Of Suspicion Points At You

Words & Music by Paul Mann & Al Lewis.

31
The Folks Who Live On The Hill

Music by Jerome Kern. Words by Oscar Hammerstein II.

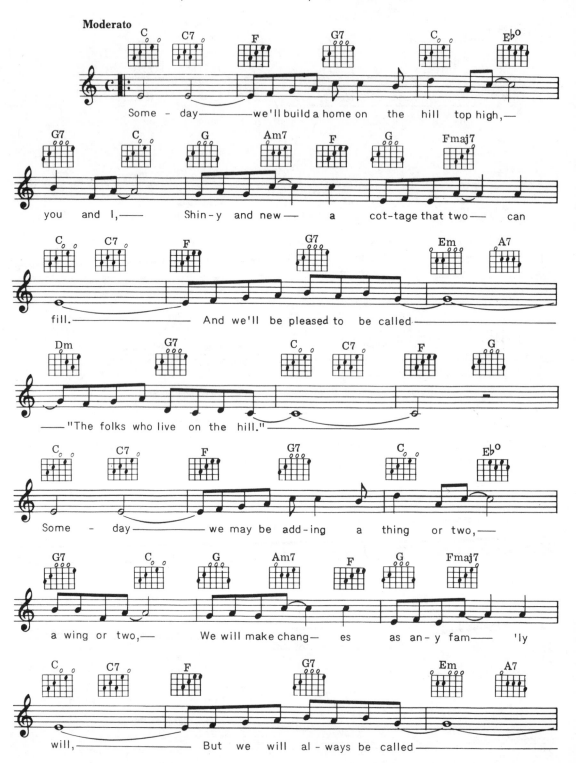

32
Funny, Familiar, Forgotten Feelings

Words & Music by Mickey Newbury.

Moderato

Last night, qui - et - ly, she walked through my mind As

I lay search - ing for sleep _____ Her soft hand reached out, she

whis - pered my name As she brushed a tear from my cheek And then those

fun - ny fa - mil - iar for - got - ten feel - ings start - ed walk - in' all

o - ver my mind It's sad, so sad to watch love go

33
Gentle On My Mind

Words & Music by John Hartford.

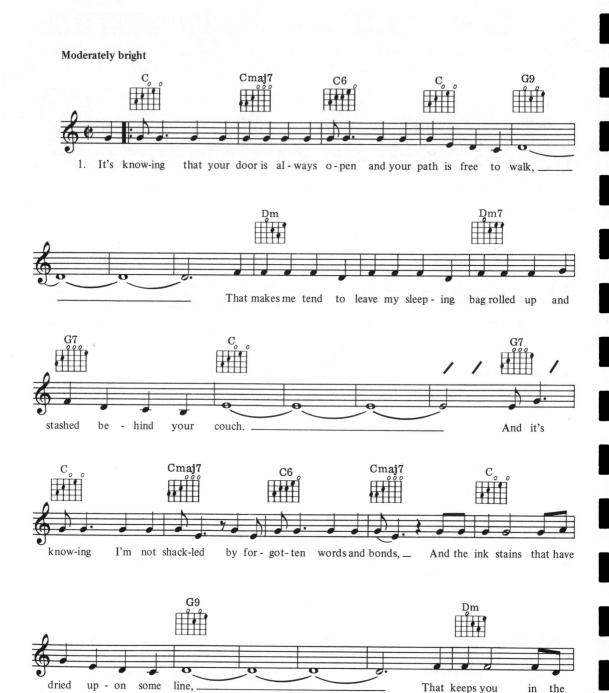

back-roads by the riv-ers   of   my mem-'ry,   That keeps you ev - er   gen-tle   on my mind.____

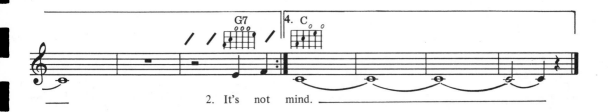

____   2. It's   not   mind. ____

VERSE 2:

It's not clinging to the rocks and ivy planted on their columns now that binds me
Or something that somebody said because they thought we fit together walkin'
It's just knowing that the world will not be cursing or forgiving
When I walk along some rail-road track and find
That you're moving on the back-roads by the rivers of my mem'ry
And for hours you're just gentle on my mind.

VERSE 3:

Though the wheat-fields and the clothes lines and the junk-yards and the highways come between us
And some other woman crying to her mother 'cause she turned and I was gone
I still might run in silence, tears of joy might stain my face
And a summer sun might burn me 'til I'm blind
But not to where I cannot see you walkin' on the back-roads
By the rivers flowing gentle on my mind.

VERSE 4:

I dip my cup of soup back from the gurglin' cracklin' cauldron in some train yard
My beard a roughning coal pile and a dirty hat pulled low across my face
Through cupped hands 'round a tin can I pretend
I hold you to my breast and find
That you're waving from the back-roads by the rivers of my mem'ry
Ever smilin', ever gentle on my mind.

34
Goodnight Tonight

Words & Music by McCartney.

Don't ___ get ___ too tired for love,

don't ___ let _____ it end.

Don't ___ say_____ good - night to love

it may nev - er___ be ___ the same ___ a -

gain. Don't say__ it don't say__ it

say an-y-thing, but don't say good-night__ to-night, don't say__ it,

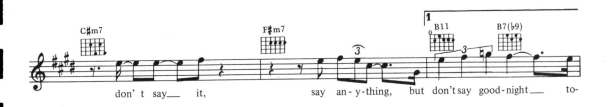

don't say__ it, say an-y-thing, but don't say good-night __ to-

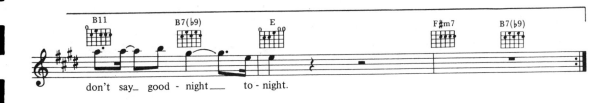

night, don't say__ it don't say__ it you can say an-y-thing, but

don't say__ good-night__ to-night.

D.%. al Coda

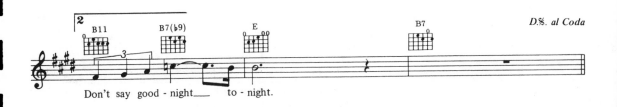

Don't say good-night__ to-night.

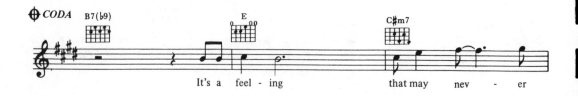

⊕ CODA

It's a feel - ing   that may   nev - er

end.   Don't say_ it,   don't say_ it

say an-y - thing, but don't say good-night_ to - night, don't say it   don't say_ it

say an-y - thing,_ but don't say good - night_ to - night, don't say _ it

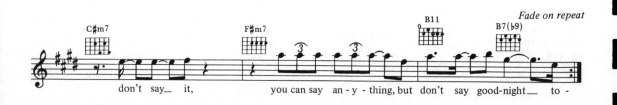

Fade on repeat

don't say_ it,   you can say an-y - thing, but don't say good-night_ to -

35
Have I Told You Lately That I Love You?

Words & Music by Scott Wiseman.

36
Green Light

Words & Music by Alan Tarney.

Moderato

Search-in' for a green light. Look-in' for it all night.

Us-ing all my keen sight Search-in' for a green light.

From just this side of mid – night, Till dawn breaks into day – light.

Keep-in' my-self —— out of sight Search-in' for a

[2nd time, instrumental 8 bars]

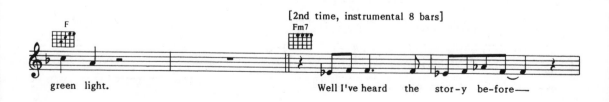

green light. Well I've heard the stor-y be-fore——

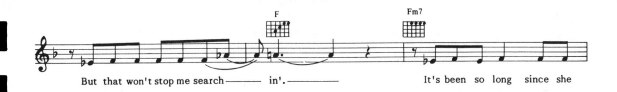

But that won't stop me search———in'.——— It's been so long since she

gave me a sign,——— A sign to stop my head turn———ing.———

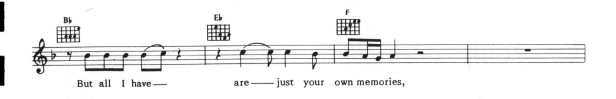

But all I have——— are——— just your own memories,

But you know ba-by, ba-by that's mine,—'Cause I'm spend-in' all——— of my time———

1. ——— Search-in' for a——————————————— 2. ——— Search-in' for a

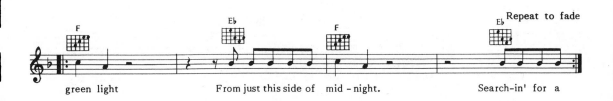

Repeat to fade

green light From just this side of mid-night. Search-in' for a

37
Guilty

Words & Music by Barry Gibb, Robin Gibb & Maurice Gibb.

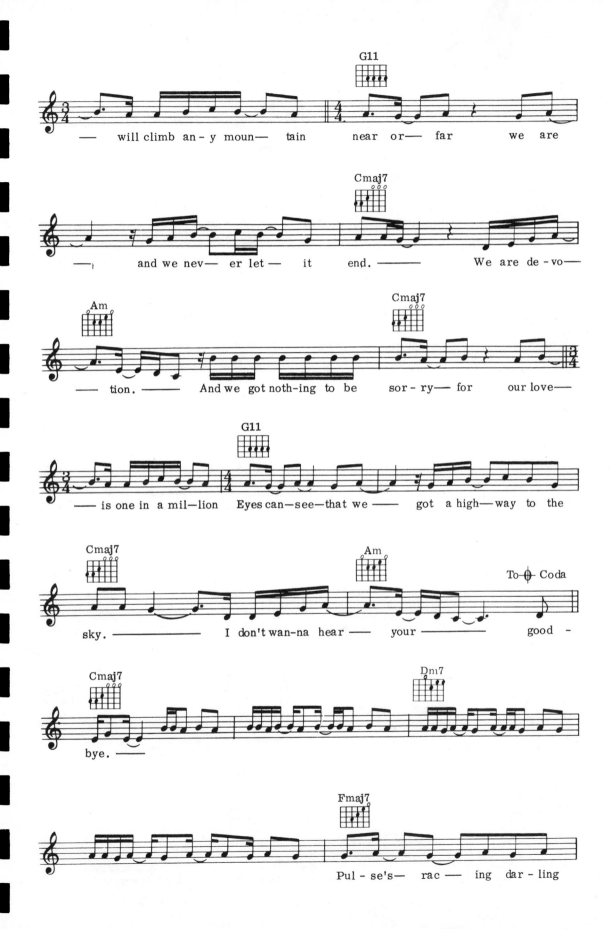

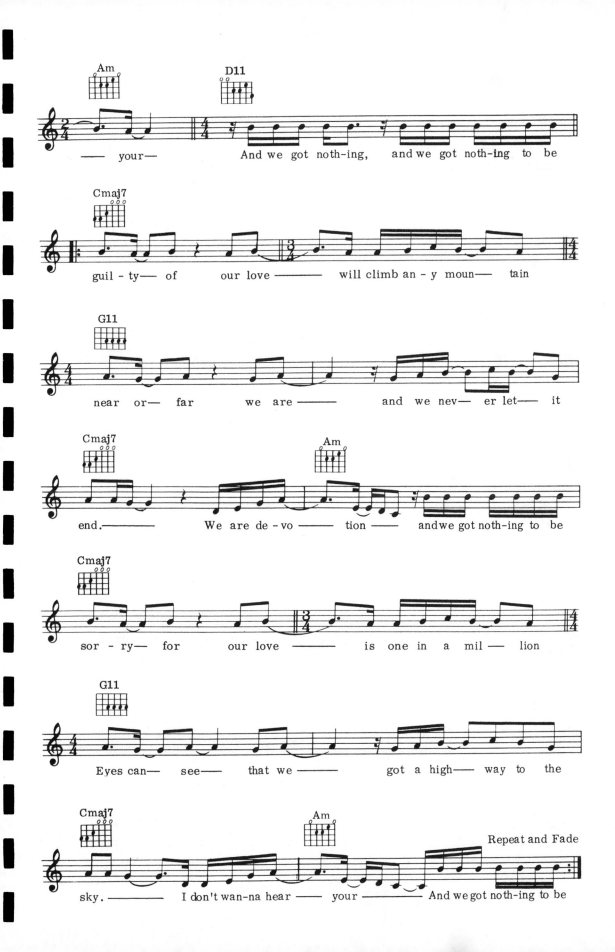

38
Hey, Good Lookin'

Words & Music by Hank Williams.

39
Heartbreaker

Words & Music by Barry Gibb, Robin Gibb & Maurice Gibb.

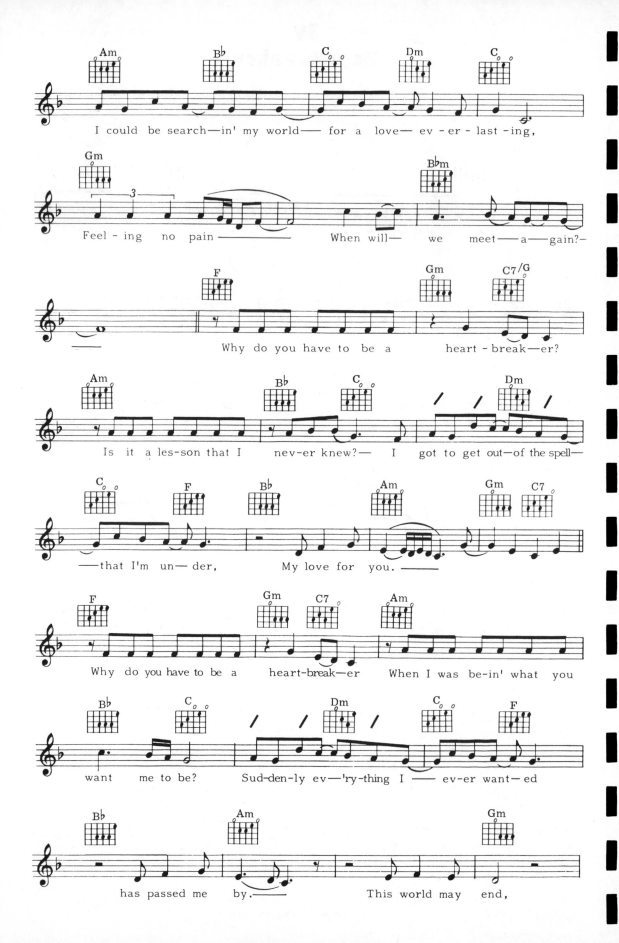

40
Here We Are

Words & Music by Gloria Estefan.

VERSE 2:

Here we are
All alone;
Trembling hearts, beating strong;
Reaching out
A breathless kiss
I never thought could feel like this.
I want to stop the time from passing by.
I wanna close my eyes
And feel your lips are touching mine.
Baby when you're close to me,
I want you more each time.
And there's nothing I can do,
To keep from loving you.

41
Hold On

Words by Carnie Wilson.
Music by Glen Ballard & Chynna Phillips.

Moderato

(1) I know there's pain — why do you lock your-self up in these chains —

— no one can change — your life ex - cept — for you — don't

ev - er let an - y - one step all ov - er you — just o - pen your heart — and your mind

— is it real - ly fair — to feel — this way in - side.

— Woh — Some-day, some - bo-dy's gon-na make you wan-na turn a-round and say goodbye —

un-til then ba-by, are you gon-na let him hold you down and make you cry, — don't you know

on — for one more day, — yeah, — hold — on —

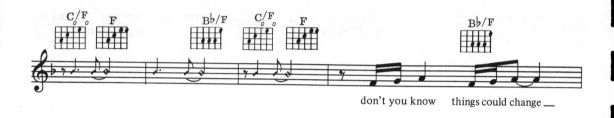

don't you know things could change —

things could go your way —— if you hold —— on —— for one

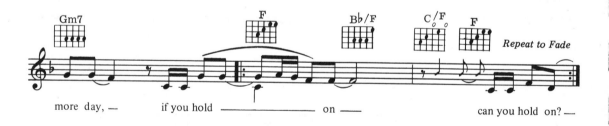

Repeat to Fade

more day, — if you hold —— on — can you hold on? —

VERSE 2

You could sustain
Mm, or are you comfortable with the pain?
You've got no one to blame for your unhappiness
No baby, you got yourself into your own mess
Ooh, lettin' your worries pass you by
Baby, don't you think it's worth your time
To change your mind?

42
Hey Jealous Lover

Words & Music by Sammy Cahn, Kay Twomey & Bee Walker.

43
I Could Have Told You

Words & Music by Carl Sigman & Arthur Williams.

44
How Am I Supposed To Live Without You

Words & Music by M. Bolton & D. James.

I could hard-ly be-lieve it when I heard the news to-day, I

had to come and get it straight from you.

They said you were leav - ing, some-one's swept your heart a-way, from the

look up-on your face I see it's true so

tell me all a-bout it, tell me 'bout the plans you're mak - ing,

tell me one thing more be-fore I go. Tell me

how I am sup-posed to live with-out you

VERSE 2:

Too proud for crying, I didn't come here to break down
It's just a dream of mine is coming to an end
And how can I blame you when I built my world around
The hope that one day we'd be so much more than friends?
I don't wanna know the price I'm gonna pay for dreaming
Even now it's more than I can take.

45
I Didn't Mean To Turn You On

Words & Music by James Harris III & Terry Lewis.

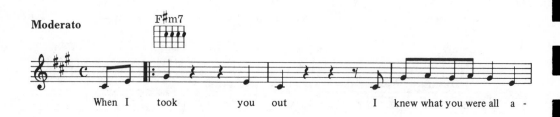

When I took you out I knew what you were all a -

bout but when I did,_____ I did - n't mean to turn you

on. Now I bring you home, you tell me

good-night's not e - nough for you, I'm sor - ry ba - by, I

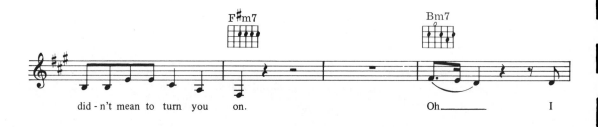

did - n't mean to turn you on. Oh_____ I

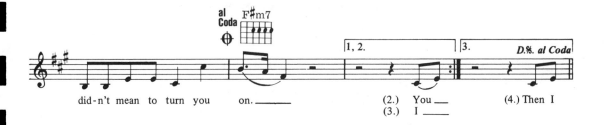

did-n't mean to turn you on. _____

(2.) You _____
(3.) I _____

(4.) Then I

on. _____   Did-n't mean to turn you on. _____

I

VERSE 2:
You read me wrong,
I wasn't trying to lead you on
Not like you think,
I didn't mean to turn you on.
I know you,
Expected a one night stand
When I refused
I knew you wouldn't understand.
I'm sorry baby,
I didn't mean to turn you on.

VERSE 3:
I told you twice
I was only trying to be nice
Only trying to be nice,
Oh, I didn't mean to turn you on.
Hey now why should I
Feel guilty 'cause I won't give,
Guilty 'cause I won't give in,
I didn't mean to turn you on.
Oh, I didn't mean to turn you on.

VERSE 4: (𝄋)
Then I took you out,
I knew what you were all about
But when I did,
I didn't mean to turn you on,
Oh, I didn't mean to turn you on.

46
I'm Gonna Sit Right Down And
Write Myself A Letter

Words by Joe Young. Music by Fred E. Ahlert.

47
I'll Get By

Words by Roy Turk. Music by Fred E. Ahlert.

48
I'm Not In Love

Words & Music by Eric Stewart & Graham Gouldman.

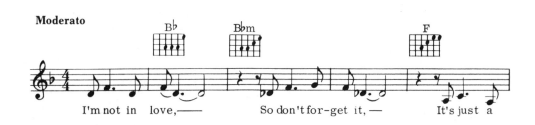

Moderato

I'm not in love,—— So don't for-get it, — It's just a

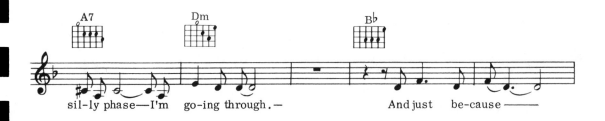

sil-ly phase—I'm go-ing through.— And just be-cause——

I call you up, —— Don't get me wrong, Don't think you've got it made.—

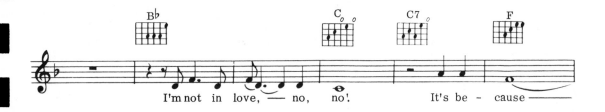

I'm not in love, — no, no! It's be - cause——

I like to see you But then a-

49
In Dreams

Words & Music by Roy Orbison.

50
I Saw The Light

Words & Music by Hank Williams.

51
Islands In The Stream

Words & Music by Barry Gibb, Maurice Gibb & Robin Gibb.

Ten-der love is blind, It re-quires — a ded-i - ca-tion.
No more will you cry. Ba-by I — will hurt you nev-er. We

All this love— we feel needs no con - ver - sa - tion we }
start and end— as one in love for - ev -er we can }

ride it to-gether ah - ah — mak-in' love — with each oth-er ah -

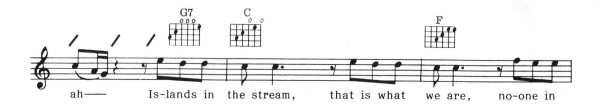

ah — Is-lands in the stream, that is what we are, no-one in

be-tween, How can we be wrong, sail a-way with me to an-oth-

er world, and we re - ly on each other ah ah — from one lov—

Repeat and Fade

52
Let's Have A Quiet Night In

Words & Music by Tony Macauley.

Moderato

To - night to-night—let's not go an-y-where, — let's
night to-night—let's not see an-y-one, — if the

turn the latch— on the door. And if the phone should ring—then let's just
par-ty's on— we're not free. I hard-ly see you now—more than a

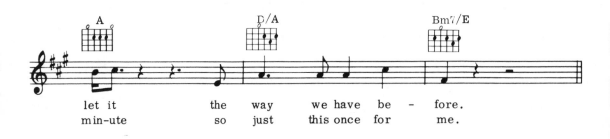

let it the way we have be - fore.
min-ute so just this once for me.

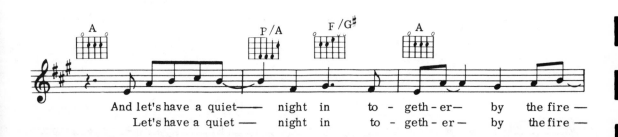

And let's have a quiet—— night in to - geth - er— by the fire —
Let's have a quiet — night in to - geth - er— by the fire —

side.— We can talk with-out an-y-one—
side.— We can dance in the can-dle-light—

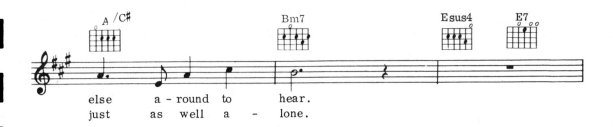

else a-round to hear.
just as well a-lone.

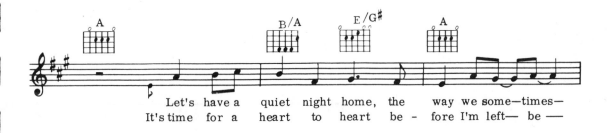

Let's have a quiet night home, the way we some—times—
It's time for a heart to heart be-fore I'm left— be —

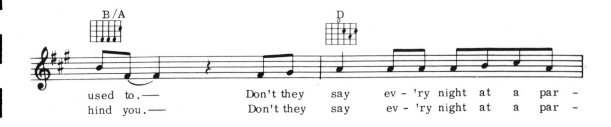

used to.— Don't they say ev-'ry night at a par-
hind you.— Don't they say ev-'ry night at a par-

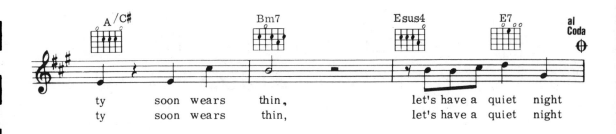

ty soon wears thin, let's have a quiet night
ty soon wears thin, let's have a quiet night

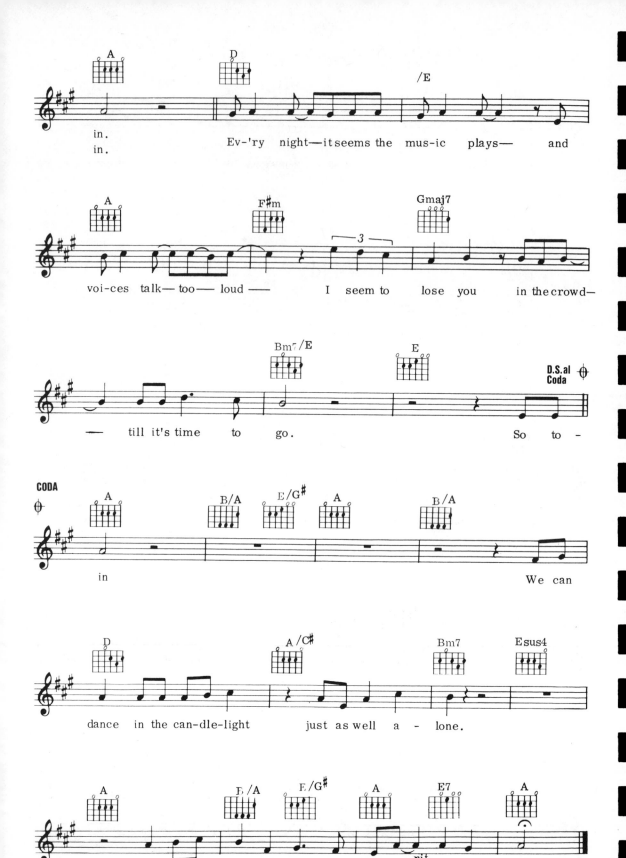

53
I Wish It Would Rain Down

Words & Music by Phil Collins.

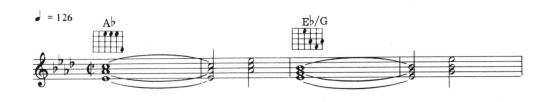

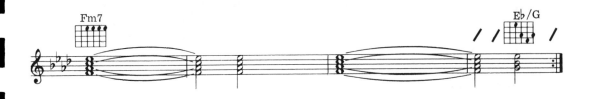

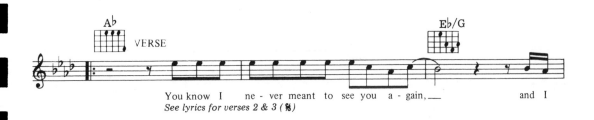

You know I ne-ver meant to see you a-gain,____ and I
See lyrics for verses 2 & 3 (%)

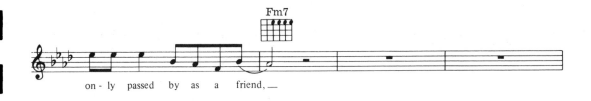

on-ly passed by as a friend, ____

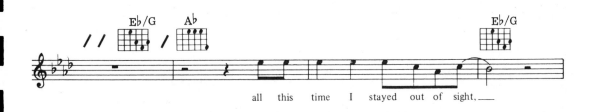

all this time I stayed out of sight, ____

in - side, _____ and I know, _ oh it's eat -

ing me, it's eat - ing me through eve-ry night _____ and day, _ I'm just

wait - ing on _____ your sign. _____

D.%. al Coda ⊕ **CODA**

Ad libs to end

Just let it rain. _____

VERSE 2:
You said you didn't need me in your life,
Oh I guess you were right,
Ooh I never meant to cause you no pain,
But it looks like I did it again.

VERSE 3:
'Cos I know, I know I never meant to cause you no pain,
And I realise I let you down,
But I know in my heart of hearts,
I know I'm never gonna hold you again.

54
Jealous Guy

Words & Music by John Lennon.

1. I was dreaming of the past ⎯
2. I was feel-ing in - se-cure ⎯
3. (Whistle) - - - - - - - - - - - - - - - - - -
4. I was trying to catch your eyes ⎯

and my heart ⎯ was beat-ing fast ⎯
you might not love ⎯ me an ⎯ y more ⎯
- - - - - - - - - - - - - - - - - - -
thought that you ⎯ was try-ing to hide ⎯

I be-gan ⎯ to lose con-trol ⎯
I was shiv ⎯ er - ing ⎯ in-side ⎯
- - - - - - - - - - - - - - - - - - -
I was swal ⎯ low - ing ⎯ my pain ⎯

55
The Last Time I Saw Paris

Music by Jerome Kern. Words by Oscar Hammerstein II.

Moderato

The last time I saw Par - is Her

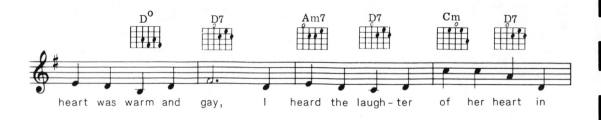

heart was warm and gay, I heard the laugh - ter of her heart in

ev - 'ry street ca - fe. The last time I saw Par - is, Her

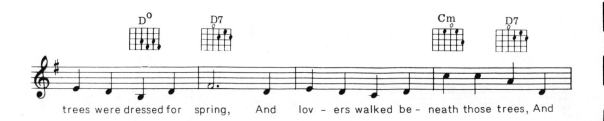

trees were dressed for spring, And lov - ers walked be - neath those trees, And

birds found songs to sing.   I dodged the same old tax – i cabs that

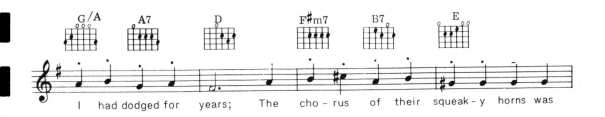

I had dodged for years;   The cho – rus of their squeak – y horns was

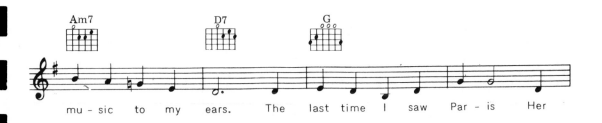

mu – sic to my ears.   The last time I saw Par – is   Her

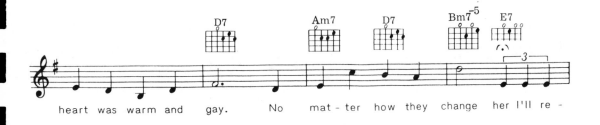

heart was warm and gay.   No mat – ter how they change her I'll re –

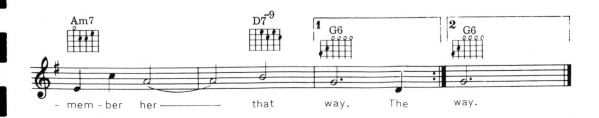

– mem – ber her ———— that way.   The   way.

56
(Let's Go To) San Francisco

Words & Music by John Carter & Ken Lewis.

Moderato

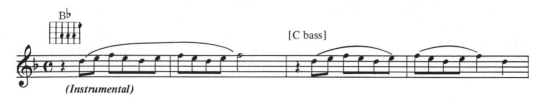

(Instrumental)

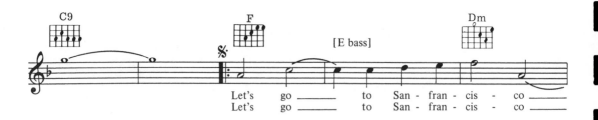

Let's go ____ to San - fran - cis - co ____
Let's go ____ to San - fran - cis - co ____

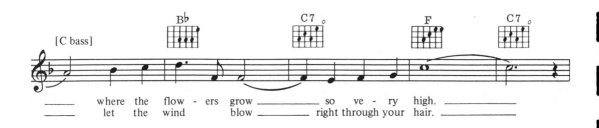

____ where the flow - ers grow ____ so ve - ry high. ____
____ let the wind blow ____ right through your hair. ____

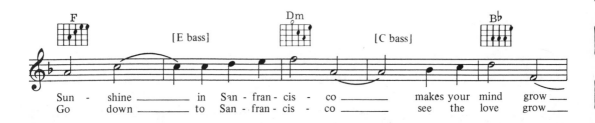

Sun - shine ____ in San - fran - cis - co ____ makes your mind grow ____
Go down ____ to San - fran - cis - co ____ see the love grow ____

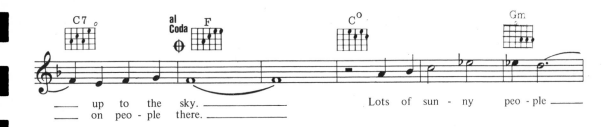

_____ up to the sky. _____ Lots of sun - ny peo - ple _____
_____ on peo - ple there. _____

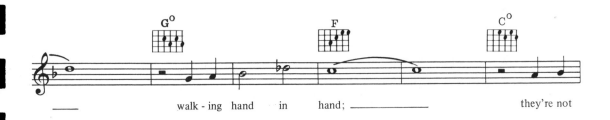

_____ walk - ing hand in hand; _____ they're not

fun - ny peo - ple, _____ they have found their

land. _____ Let's go, let's go Let's go to San - Fran - cis - co.

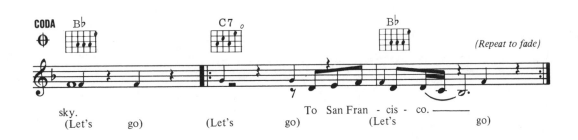

sky. To San Fran - cis - co. _____
(Let's go) (Let's go) (Let's go)

57
Lily Was Here

Music by David A. Stewart.

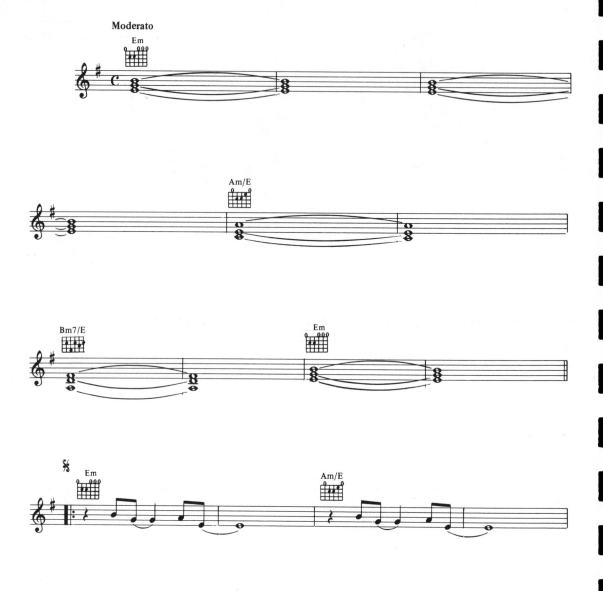

D.S. (Rpt.) Ad lib. to Fade

58
Magical Mystery Tour

Words & Music by John Lennon & Paul McCartney.

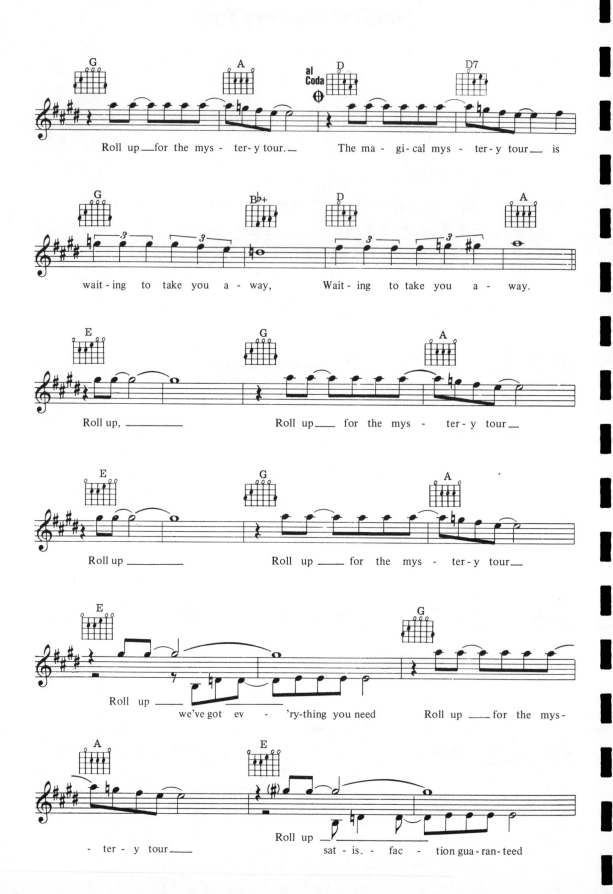

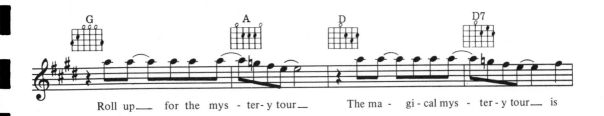

Roll up___ for the mys - ter- y tour___ The ma - gi - cal mys - ter- y tour___ is

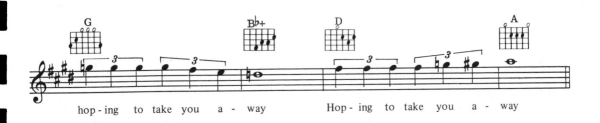

hop - ing to take you a - way   Hop - ing to take you a - way

Slower tempo

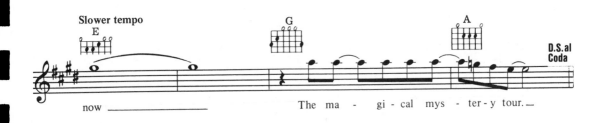

D.S. al Coda

now _____   The ma - gi - cal mys - ter- y tour. —

CODA

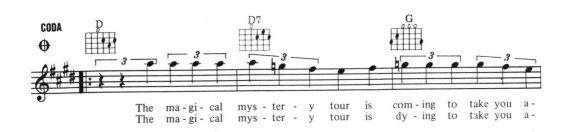

The ma - gi - cal mys - ter - y tour is com - ing to take you a-
The ma - gi - cal mys - ter - y tour is dy - ing to take you a-

way,   Com - ing to take you a - way.
way,   Dy - ing to take you a -   way, take you a - way.

59
Little Boat (O Barquinho)

Music by Roberto Menescal.
Original Words by Ronaldo Boscoli.
English Lyric by Buddy Kaye.

60
Look For The Silver Lining

Music by Jerome Kern. Words by Buddy De Sylva.

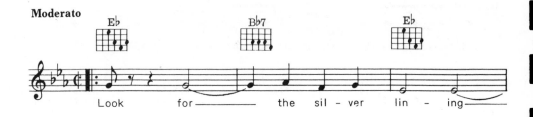

Look for the sil - ver lin - ing

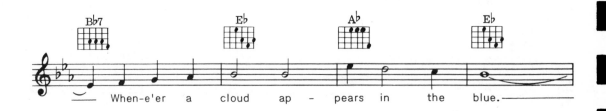

When-e'er a cloud ap - pears in the blue.

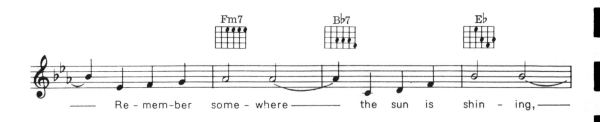

Re - mem-ber some - where the sun is shin - ing,

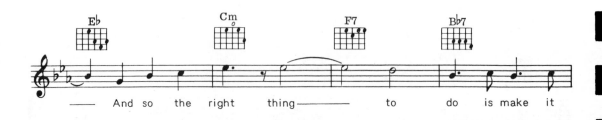

And so the right thing to do is make it

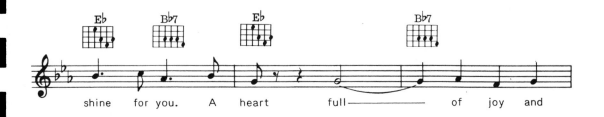

shine   for you.   A   heart   full——————   of   joy   and

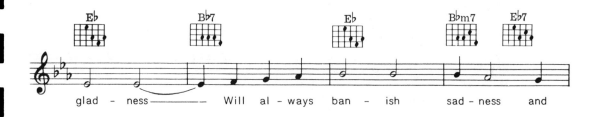

glad - ness————   Will   al - ways   ban - ish   sad - ness   and

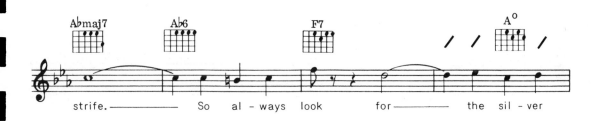

strife.————   So   al - ways   look   for————   the   sil - ver

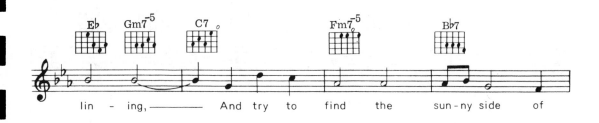

lin - ing,————   And   try   to   find   the   sun - ny side   of

life!

life!————

61
Make Believe

Music by Jerome Kern. Words by Oscar Hammerstein II.

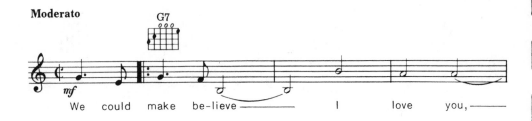

We could make be-lieve —— I love you,

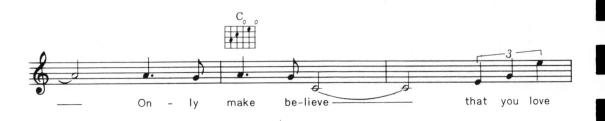

—— On - ly make be-lieve —— that you love

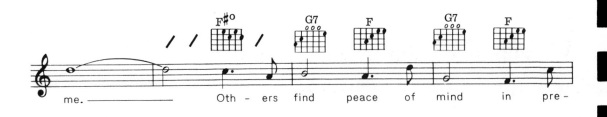

me. —— Oth - ers find peace of mind in pre-

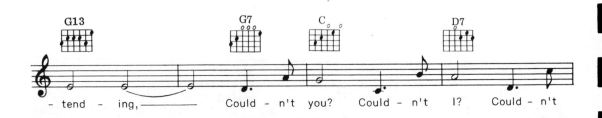

- tend - ing, —— Could - n't you? Could - n't I? Could - n't

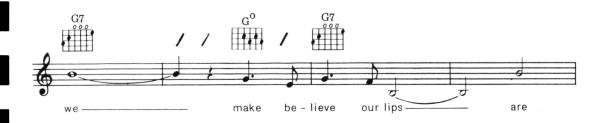

we _____ make be - lieve our lips _____ are

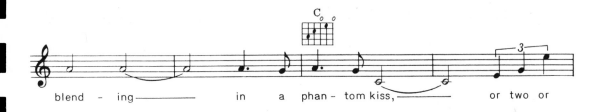

blend - ing _____ in a phan - tom kiss, _____ or two or

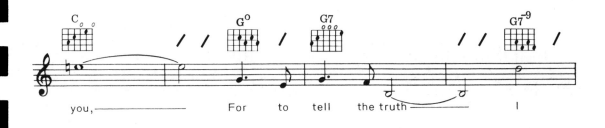

three? _____ Might as well make be - lieve I love

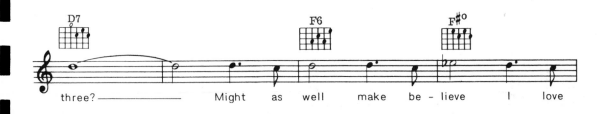

you, _____ For to tell the truth _____ I

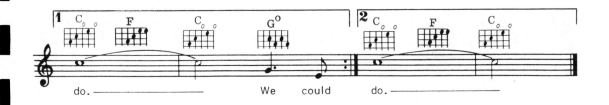

do. _____ We could do. _____

62
Mary Had A Little Lamb

Words & Music by McCartney.

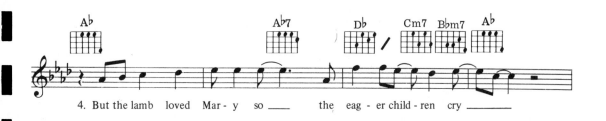

4. But the lamb loved Mar - y so ___ the eag - er child - ren cry ___

And Mar - y loves the lamb ___ you know ___ the teach - er did ___ re - ply.___

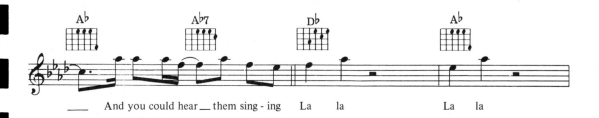

___ And you could hear ___ them sing - ing La la La la

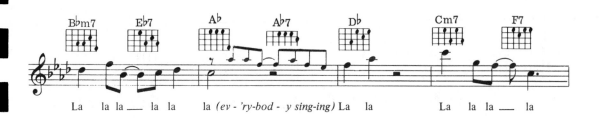

La la la ___ la la la (ev - 'ry - bod - y sing - ing) La la La la la ___ la

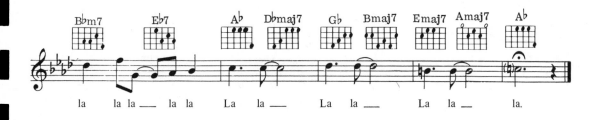

la la la ___ la la La la ___ La la ___ La la ___ la.

3. Soon the teacher turned it out
   Still it lingered near —
   Waited patiently about till
   Mary did appear - you could hear them singing

   (To Chorus)

63
Moments To Remember

Words & Music by Robert Allen & Al Stillman.

Moderately slow (with feeling)

The New Year's Eve we did the town, the day we tore the
qui - et walks, the nois - y fun, the ball - room prize we

goal -post down.
al - most won. We will have these Mo - ments To Re - mem - ber. The

mem - ber. Tho' sum -mer turns to win - ter and the pre - sent dis - ap -

pears, The laugh - ter we were glad to share will e - cho thru the

years. When oth - er nights and oth - er days may find us gone our

sep' -rate ways. We will have these Mo - ments To Re - mem - ber. _____

64
Monday Monday

Words & Music by John Phillips.

Steady Rock

Mon - day, Mon - day, so good to me
- day, can't trust that day

Mon - day morn - in', it was all I hoped it would be.
Mon - day, Mon - day, some - times it just turns out that way.

Oh, Mon - day morn - in', Mon - day morn - in' could - n't guar - an - tee
Oh, Mon - day morn - in', you give me no warn - in' of what was to be

That Mon - day ev - nin' you would still be here with me.
Oh, Mon - day, Mon - day how could you leave and not take

1. Mon - day, Mon -

2. me. Ev - 'ry oth - er day, — ev - 'ry oth - er day, ev - 'ry oth - er day of the week is

fine, yeah! — But when - ev - er Mon - day comes. but when - ev - er Mon - day comes you can find me

cry'n. yeah! — *tacet* **D.S. & fade** Mon - day, Mon -

65
Nikita

Words & Music by Elton John & Bernie Taupin.

66
Nothing Ever Happens

Words & Music by Justin Currie.

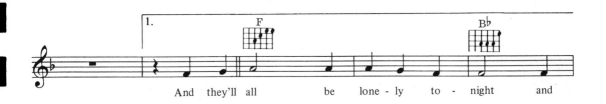

And they'll all   be   lone - ly   to - night   and

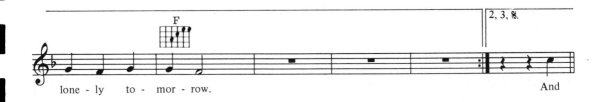

lone - ly   to - mor - row.   And

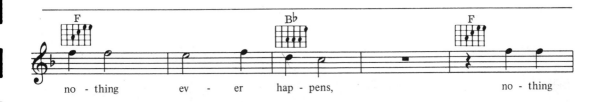

no - thing   ev - er   hap - pens,   no - thing

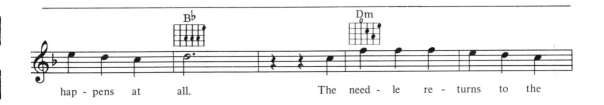

hap - pens   at   all.   The   need - le   re - turns   to   the

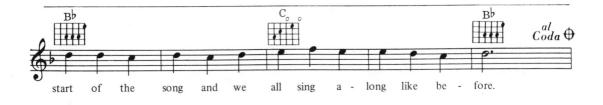

start   of   the   song   and   we   all   sing   a - long   like   be - fore.

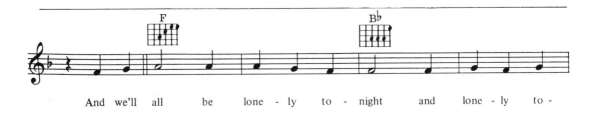

And we'll   all   be   lone - ly   to - night   and   lone - ly   to -

Sy - na - gogues at six o' - clock and we'll all go a - long like be -

fore. And we'll all be lone - ly to - night and

lone - ly to - mor - row. _____

VERSE 2:
Gentlemen time please, you know we can't serve anymore
Now the traffic lights change to stop, when there's nothing to go
And by five o'clock everything's dead
And every third car is a cab
And ignorant people sleep in their beds
Like the doped white mice in the college lab.

VERSE 3:
Telephone exchanges click while there's nobody there
The Martians could land in the carpark and no one would care
Closed-circuit cameras in department stores
Shoot the same movie every day
And the stars of these films neither die nor get killed
Just survive constant action replay.

VERSE 4:
And bill hoardings advertise products that nobody needs
While angry of Manchester writes to complain about
All the repeats on T.V.
And computer terminals report some gains
On the values of copper and tin
While American businessmen snap up Van Goghs
For the price of a hospital wing.

67
Ocean Deep

Words & Music by Rodney Trott & Jonathan Sweet.

Love, can't you see__ I'm a - lone,____
Love, I've been search - ing so long,____
Love, can't you hear__ when I call,____

can't you give__ this fool a chance?__ A lit - tle love is all I
I've been search - ing high and low.____ A lit - tle love is all I
can't you hear__ a word I say?__ A lit - tle love is all I

ask, a lit - tle kind - ness in the night.____
ask, a lit - tle sad - ness when you go.____
ask, a lit - tle feel - ing when we touch.____

Please don't leave__ me be - hind,__ no, don't tell__ me love is
May - be you__ need a friend,__ on - ly please don't let's pre -
Why am I__ still a - lone?__ I've got a heart with - out a

oth - er, and as I cry my - self to____ sleep____

I know this love of mine will keep,____ oc - ean

To Coda ⊕ *D.C.*

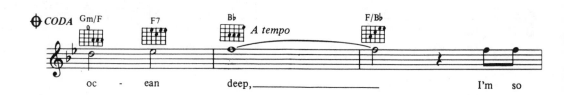

⊕ *CODA*

oc - ean deep,_____ I'm so

A tempo

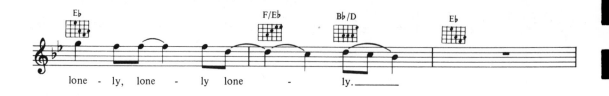

lone - ly, lone - ly lone - ly.____

Oc - ean deep,____
Poco rall. on my own in my room____
I'm so lone-ly oh so lone - ly

A tempo

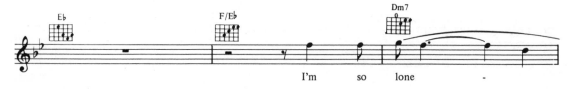

I'm so lone -

- ly.____   Oc - ean

Repeat to Fade

68
Only The Lonely

Words & Music by Roy Orbison & Joe Melson.

On - ly the lone - ly know the way I feel to - night ____ On - ly the

lone - ly know this feel - ing ain't right ____ There goes my ba - by ____

____ There goes my heart ____ They've gone for - ev - er ____ So far a -

part ____ But on - ly the lone - ly ____ know ____ why ____

____ I cry ____ On - ly the lone - ly ____ On - ly the lone - ly.

2.
Only the lonely know the heartaches I've been through
Only the lonely know I cry and cry for you
Maybe tomorrow, a new romance
No more sorrow, but that's the chance
You've got to take if you're lonely
Heartbreak, Only the lonely.

69
Oh, Lonesome Me

Words & Music by Don Gibson.

70
Please Don't Fall In Love

Words & Music by Mike Batt.

Slow ballad tempo

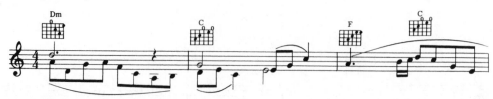

I know that you're with— him Just now as I write,— I

know you need some— one To hold you at night,— But I'm beg-ging you, Ba — by,

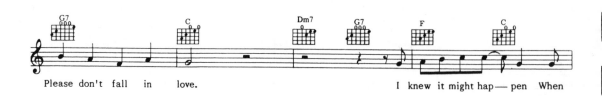

Please don't fall in love. I knew it might hap— pen When

I was a - way— And now that it's hap— pened I just want to say— That I'm

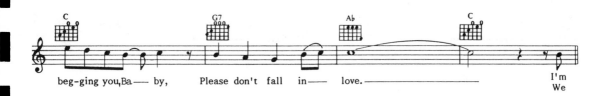

beg-ging you, Ba — by, Please don't fall in — love. ———— I'm
We

us - ual - ly strong———— But I'm feel - ing so weak, ——— It
kissed at the air———port, We said we could wait, ——— I be-lieve—

wells up in - side——— me, I cry when I speak. ——— But the
——— it is we——— Who de-ter——— mine our fate; ——— And I

more I call you on the phone, The more I feel a-lone,—
love you more than I can say Don't throw it all a-way,—

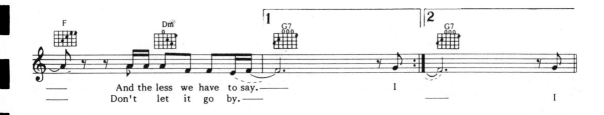

——— And the less we have to say.——— I
——— Don't let it go by.——— ——— I

know that you're with——— him   Just   now   as   I   write,——   I

know you need some—one   To   hold you at night,——   But   I'm   beg-ging you, Ba——by,

Please   don't   fall   in   love.   I

know you don't tell—— me   To   spare me the pain,——   Don't   want you to tell—— me,   I

don't need his name,——   But   I'm   beg-ging you, Ba——by,   Please   don't   fall   in———

Slow

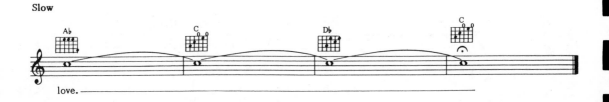

love. ———

71
Put It There

Words & Music by McCartney.

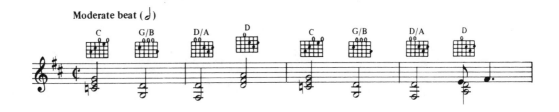

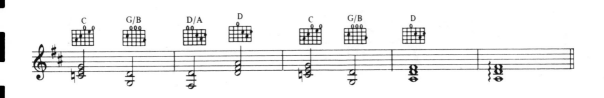

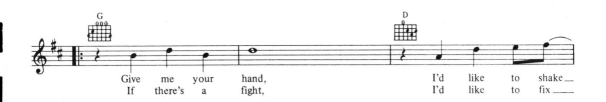

Give me your hand,   I'd like to shake___
If there's a fight,   I'd like to fix___

___ it. ___   I want to show___ you___ I'm your
___ it. ___   I hate to see___ things go so

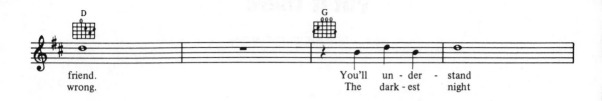

friend.
wrong.

You'll un - der - stand
The dark - est night

if I can make it clear, _____
and all its mixed e - mo - tions

it's all that
is get - ting

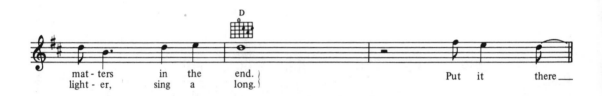

mat - ters in the end.
light - er, sing a long.

Put it there ___

___

if it weighs a ton, _____

that's what a fa - ther said _____

to his young ___ son.

I don't care _____

if it weighs a ton, ___

72
Puppy Love

Words & Music by Paul Anka.

And they called it pup-py love, _____ Oh, I guess they'll nev-er

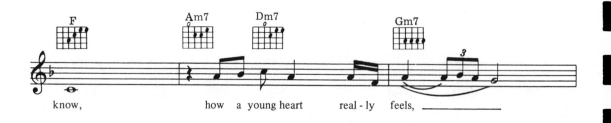

know, how a young heart real-ly feels, _____

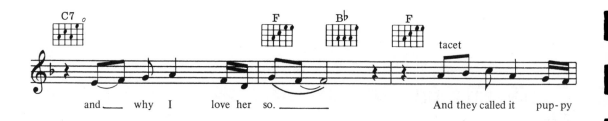

and _____ why I love her so. _____ And they called it pup-py

love _____ just be-cause we're in our teens, Tell them all it is-n't

fair _____ to take a-way my on-ly dream. _____ I

cry each night my tears _ for you, my tears are all _ in vain, _____ I'll

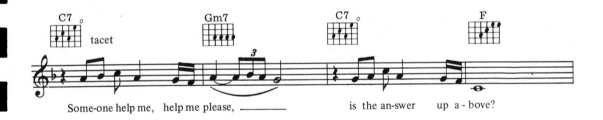

hope _ and I'll pray_ that _ may - be some-day you'll be back in my arms once a - gain

tacet

Some-one help me, help me please, _____ is the an-swer up a-bove?

How can I, how can I tell them _ This is not a pup-py love. _____

73

Queen Of The New Year

Words & Music by Ricky Ross & Jim Prime.

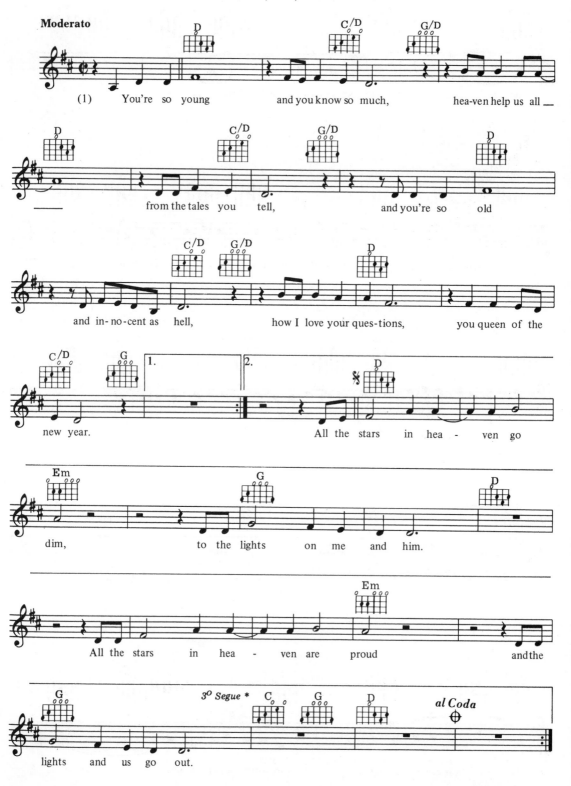

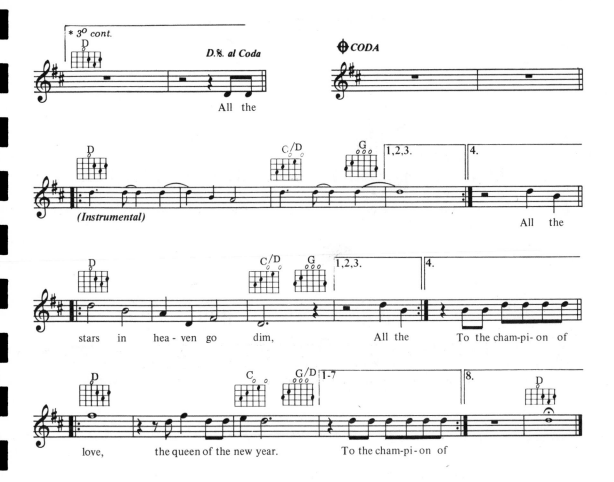

VERSE 2:
Oh you're so young
And you know so much
Oh my mind's not made up
About the way forward.
And now my heart
You know these things
My name for you
Is queen of the new year.

VERSE 3:
Now I'm telling you this
In a difficult year
You know your mother
She gave me problems.
What am I gonna do
With your honest heart
The champion of love
The queen of the new year.

74
Raining In My Heart

Words & Music by Boudleaux & Felice Bryant.

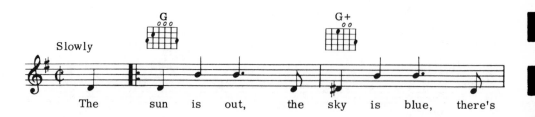

The sun is out, the sky is blue, there's

not a cloud to spoil the view—But it's rain - ing, Rain-ing in my

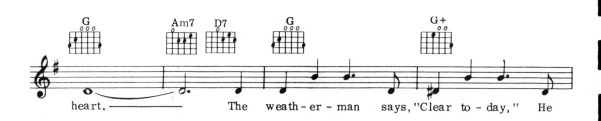

heart. _____ The weath - er - man says, "Clear to - day," He

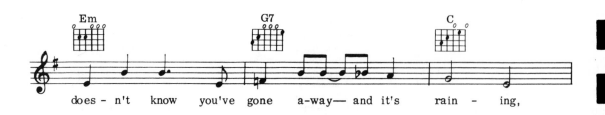

does - n't know you've gone a - way— and it's rain - ing,

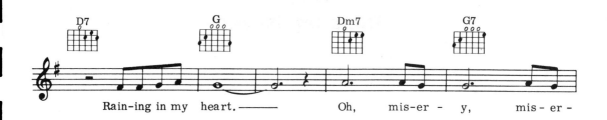

Rain-ing in my heart.———— Oh, mis-er - y, mis - er -

y,————————————— What's gon-na be-come———— of

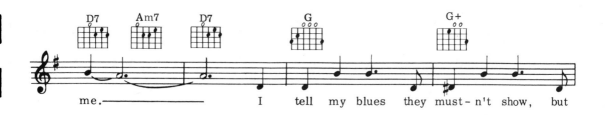

me.————————————— I tell my blues they must-n't show, but

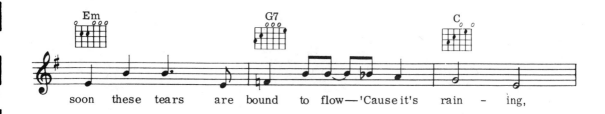

soon these tears are bound to flow—'Cause it's rain - ing,

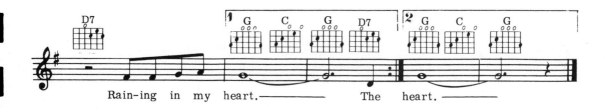

Rain-ing in my heart.———— The heart. ————

75
Running Scared

Words & Music by Roy Orbison & Joe Melson.

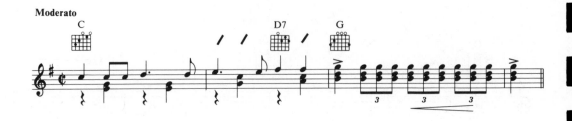

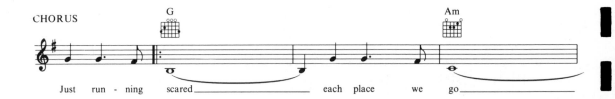

Just run-ning scared _____ each place we go _____

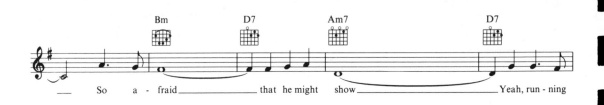

_ So a-fraid _____ that he might show _____ Yeah, run-ning

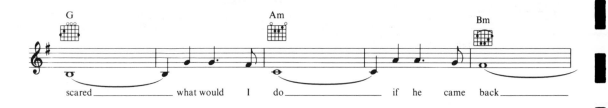

scared _____ what would I do _____ if he came back _____

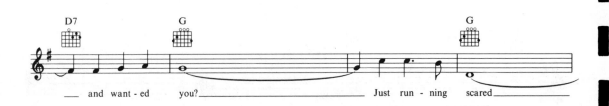

_ and want-ed you? _____ Just run-ning scared _____

76
Saviour's Day

Words & Music by Chris Eaton.

Moderato

Now we have been through the har-vest,

win - ter has tru - ly be-gun; now we are walk - ing the chill of the night, we are

wait-ing for, wait-ing for,— for the Sa-viour's Day.

Ma - ny have come from the val-leys, ma - ny have come from the hills;
Join-ing the old and the young ones, join-ing the black and the white;

ma-ny have start-ed their jour-ney home to be with someone, with someone— on the Sa-viour's
meet-ing the need of the hungry is He, will we ev - er re-member Him — on the Sa-viour's

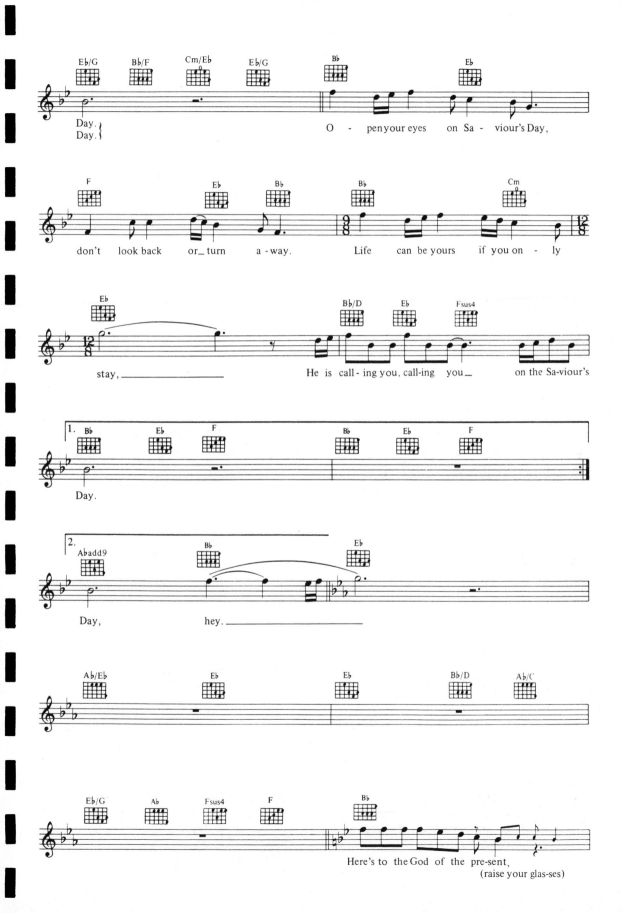

77
The Song Is You

Music by Jerome Kern. Words by Oscar Hammerstein II.

Moderato

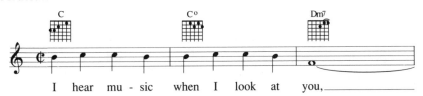

I hear mu - sic when I look at you,____

____ a beau-ti-ful theme of ev-'ry dream I ev-er knew,____

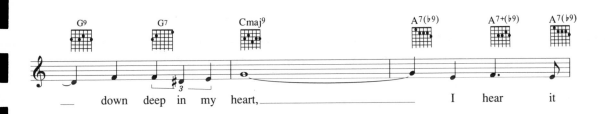

____ down deep in my heart,____ I hear it

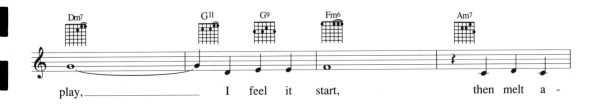

play,____ I feel it start, then melt a -

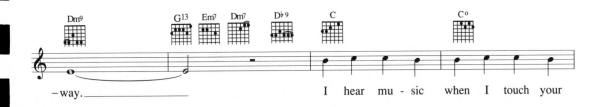

-way.____ I hear mu-sic when I touch your

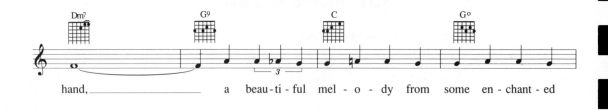

hand,_____ a beau-ti-ful mel-o-dy from some en-chant-ed

land,_____ down deep in my heart_____ I hear it

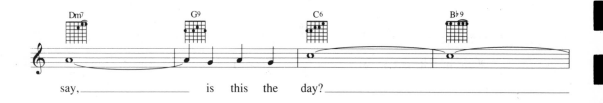

say,_____ is this the day?_____

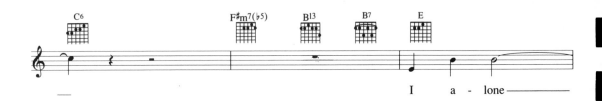

____ I a - lone_____

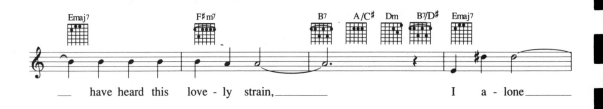

____ have heard this love-ly strain,_____ I a - lone_____

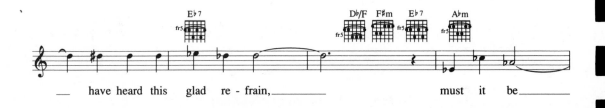

____ have heard this glad re - frain,_____ must it be_____

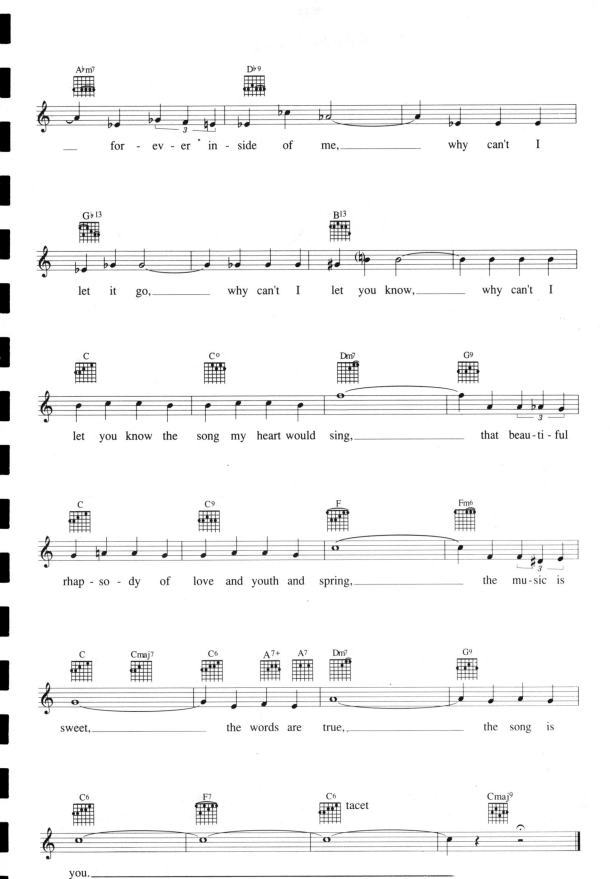

78
Silver Lady

Words & Music by Tony Macauley & Geoff Stephens.

Steady beat, not too slow

Tired of drif-ting __ search-ing __ shif-ting from
Dou-ble tal-kers __ back street __ walk-ers at

town to town, __
ev'-ry turn, __

Ev'-ry time I __ slip and slide __ a lit-tle
Seed-y mo-tels and no star ho-tels till I

fur-ther down. __
had to learn __

I can't make it if you won't take me back __ af-ter ev'-
That the one __ shin-ing thing in my life __ was the sweet

-ry-thing I put you through __ but hon-ey, you're my last __ hope and who else __
__ love I had with you __ and

79
Simon Smith And The Amazing Dancing Bear

Words & Music by Randy Newman.

I may go out to mor-row if I can bor-row a coat to wear,_
Seen at the ni-cest pla-ces where well fed fa-ces all stop to stare,_

Oh I'd step out in style_ with my sin-cere smile_ and my danc-ing bear. _Out-rage-
Mak-ing the grand-est en - trance is Si - mon Smith_ and his danc-ing bear. They'll love

- ous. a - larm-ing, cour - age - ous, charm-ing Oh who_
_ us won't they? they feed us don't they?

_ would think _ a boy _ and bear _ could be well _ ac - cept - ed ev-

- 'ry - where, ___ It's just a - maz - ing how ___ fair peo - ple can be ___

___ *(Instrumental)*

Oh who needs mon - ey

when you're fun - ny The great ___ at - trac - tion ev -

- 'ry - where ___ will be Si - mon Smith ___ and his danc - ing bear. ___ It's

Si - mon Smith ___ and the a - maz - ing ___ danc - ing ___ bear.

80
Singing The Blues

Words & Music by Melvin Endsley.

Moderato

Well I nev-er felt more like sing-ing the blues— 'cause

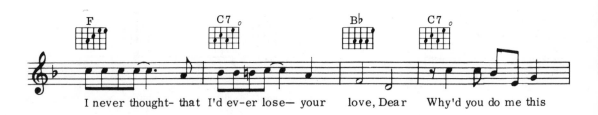

I never thought- that I'd ev-er lose— your love, Dear Why'd you do me this

way?———— Well, I nev-er felt more like cry-ing all night— 'cause

ev-'ry-thing's wrong— and noth-ing ain't right— with - out you

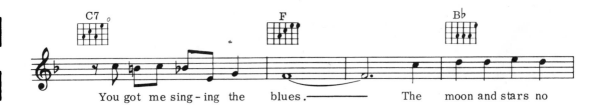

You got me sing-ing the blues.———— The moon and stars no

long-er shine, the dream is gone I thought was mine There's noth-ing left for

me to do but cry———— o-ver you— Well, I nev-er felt more like

run-ning a-way— but why should I go— 'cause I could-n't stay— with-out you

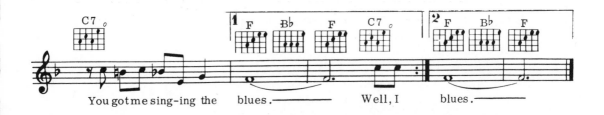

You got me sing-ing the blues.———— Well, I blues.————

81
Sunshine, Lollipops And Rainbows

Music by Marvin Hamlisch. Words by Howard Liebling.

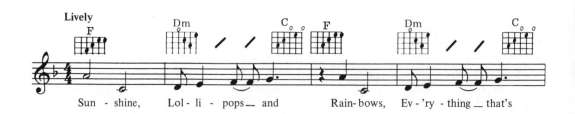

Sun - shine, Lol - li - pops— and Rain - bows, Ev - 'ry - thing — that's

won - der - ful is what I feel — when we're to - geth - er;

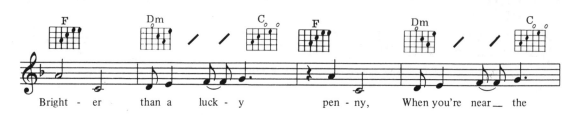

Bright - er than a luck - y pen - ny, When you're near — the

rain goes, Dis - ap - pears, dear and I feel so fine.

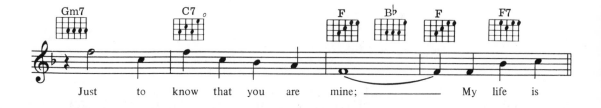

Just to know that you are mine; —————— My life is

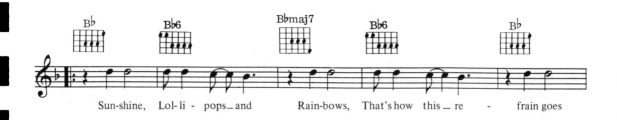

Sun-shine, Lol-li - pops— and Rain-bows, That's how this — re - frain goes

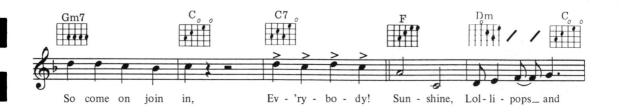

So come on join in, Ev - 'ry - bo - dy! Sun - shine, Lol - li - pops— and

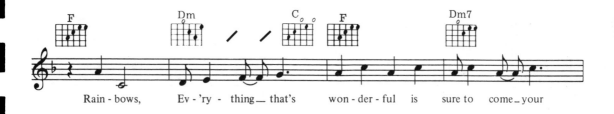

Rain - bows, Ev - 'ry - thing— that's won - der - ful is sure to come— your

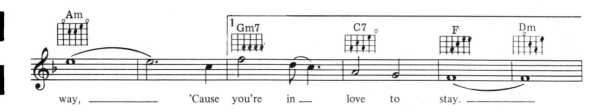

way, _____ 'Cause you're in — love to stay. _____

My life is you're in love, you're in love, And

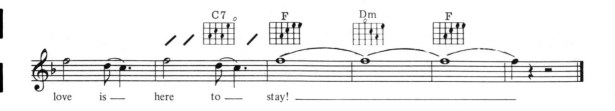

love is — here to — stay! _____

82
Those Good Old Dreams

Music by Richard Carpenter. Words by John Bettis.

As a child ___ I was known ___ of a long-

___ for make-be-lieve-in' All a-lone ___ I cre-at-ed fan-ta-sies
-for-got-ten fire ___ You're a touch of a slow-ly grow-in' wind

___ As I grew ___ peo-ple called ___ it self-de-ceiv-in'
You're a taste ___ of the ev-er chang-in' sea-sons

But my heart ___ helped me hold ___ the mem-o-ries ___
Tell-in' me ___ there are some-things that don't end ___

As I walk thru the world ___ I find a-round ___ me
We have left all the dark-ness far be-hind ___ us

Some-thin' new ___ yet fa-mil-iar's in the air ___ I feel it ev-'ry-
All those hopes ___ that we held a-long the way ___ have made it to ___ this

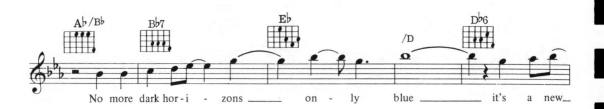

No more dark hor-i - zons ____ on - ly blue ____ it's a new_

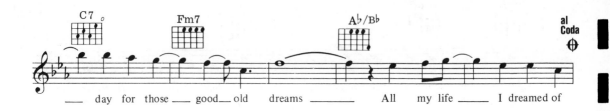

____ day for those ___ good___ old dreams ____ All my life ____ I dreamed of

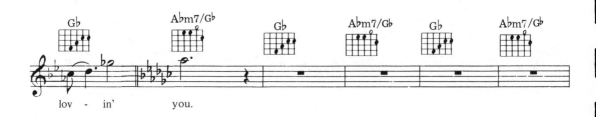

lov - in' you.

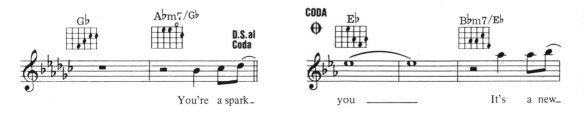

You're a spark_ you ____ It's a new_

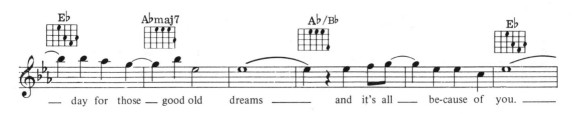

___ day for those ___ good old dreams ____ and it's all ___ be-cause of you. ___

Repeat to fade

83
Take These Chains From My Heart

Words & Music by Fred Rose & Hy Heath.

Moderato

1. Take these chains from my heart and set me free _____ You've grown
2. (Give my) heart just a word of sym-pa-thy _____ Be as

cold and no long-er care for me _____ All my faith in you is
fair to my heart as you can be _____ Then if you no long-er

gone but the heart-aches ling-er on Take these chains from my heart and set me
care for the love that's beat-ing there Take these chains from my heart and set me

free _____ Take these tears from my eyes and let me see _____
free _____ Take these chains from my heart and set me free _____

_____ Just a spark of the love that used to be _____ If you
_____ You've grown cold and no long-er care for me _____ All my

love some-bo-dy new, let me find a new love too Take these chains from my
faith in you is gone but the heart-aches ling-er on Take these chains from my

1. F
2. F Bb F

heart and set me free. _____ 2. Give my
heart and set me free. _____ free.

84
Thank You For Being A Friend

Words & Music by Andrew Gold.

Thank-you for be - ing a friend, ——

Trav - elled down the road and back a - gain. —— Your

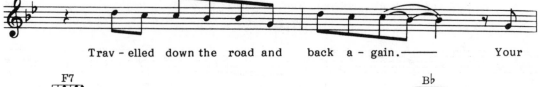

heart is true — you're a pal and a con - fi - dant. ——

I'm not a-shamed— to say ——

I hope it al - ways will stay —— this way.— My

hat is off— won't you stand up and take a bow? ——

And if you threw a par —— ty, in -

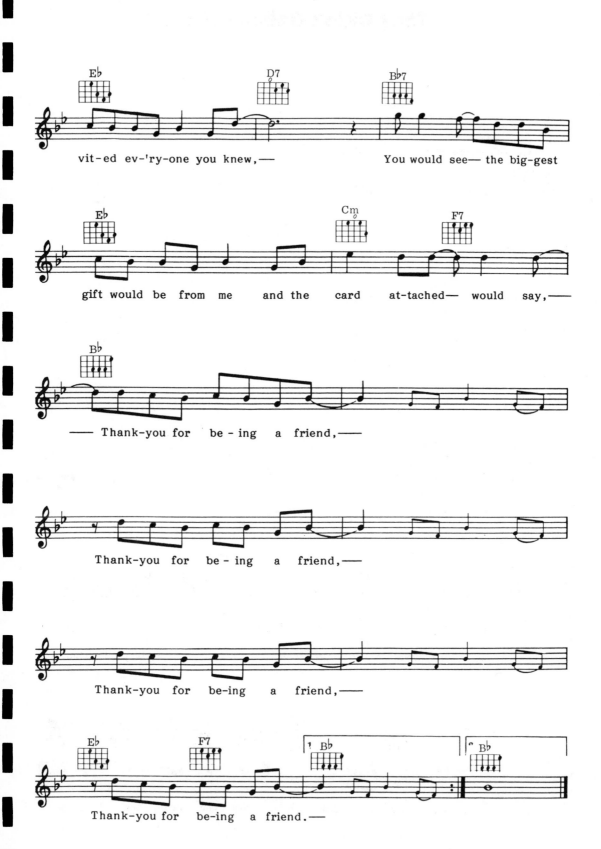

85
They Didn't Believe Me

Music by Jerome Kern. Words by Herbert Reynolds.

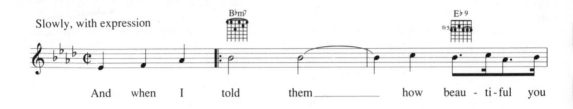

Slowly, with expression

And when I told them_____ how beau - ti - ful you

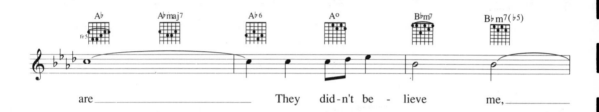

are_____ They did - n't be - lieve me,_____

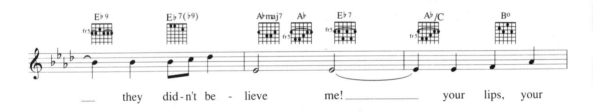

___ they did - n't be - lieve me!_____ your lips, your

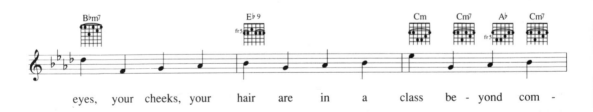

eyes, your cheeks, your hair are in a class be - yond com -

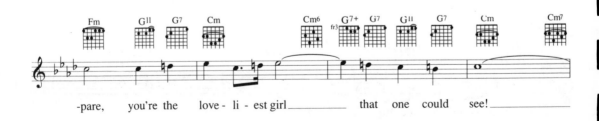

-pare, you're the love - li - est girl_____ that one could see!_____

86
This Masquerade

Words & Music by Leon Russell.

87
Too Much Heaven

Words & Music by Barry Gibb, Robin Gibb & Maurice Gibb.

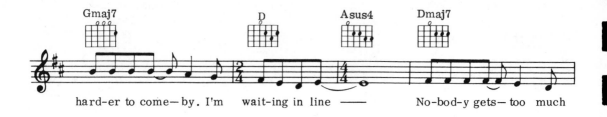

No - bod - y gets — too much hea-ven no more.— It's much

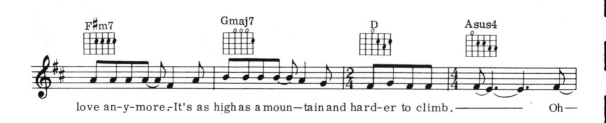

hard-er to come—by. I'm wait-ing in line —— No-bod-y gets— too much

love an-y-more.—It's as high as a moun—tain and hard-er to climb.———— Oh—

— You and me, girl, ——
{ got a lot —— of love in store   And it
{ got a high —way to the sky.   We can

flows through you and it flows through me And I   love you so much more than my
turn a - way from the night and day And the   tears we had to cry. You're my

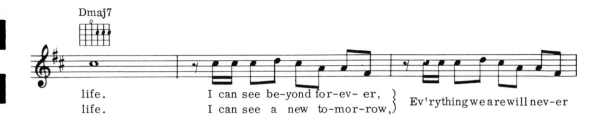

life.   I can see be-yond for-ev- er, }

life.   I can see a new to-mor-row, } Ev'rything we are will nev-er

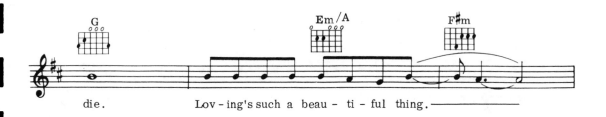

die.   Lov-ing's such a beau - ti - ful thing.——

Oh,   you   make my world —— a sum-mer day.— Are you

When   you   are to me —— the light a-bove——There for

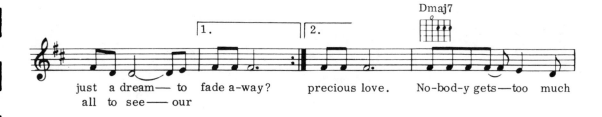

just a dream— to fade a-way?   precious love. No-bod-y gets—too much

all to see—— our

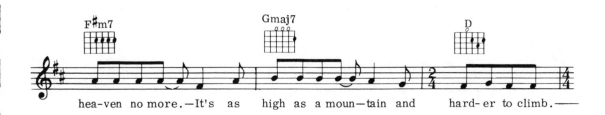

hea-ven no more.—It's as   high as a moun-tain and   hard-er to climb.——

Oh

Lov-ing's such a beau-ti-ful thing ——— You make my world —— a

summer day.— Are you just a dream —— to fade ——————— a-

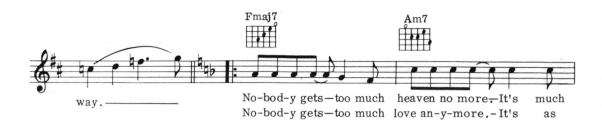

way. ——————— No-bod-y gets—too much heaven no more.—It's much
No-bod-y gets—too much love an-y-more.-It's as

Repeat & fade

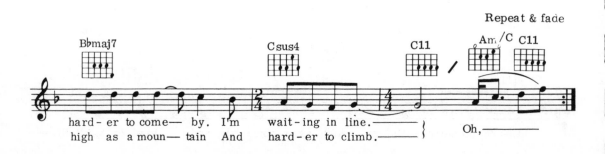

hard-er to come— by. I'm wait-ing in line.——— Oh,———
high as a moun—tain And hard-er to climb.———

88
Unchained Melody

Music by Alex North. Words by Hy Zaret.

Moderato

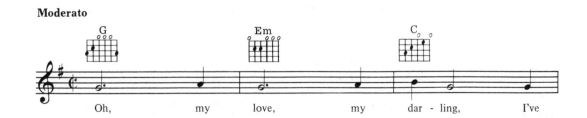

Oh, my love, my dar - ling, I've

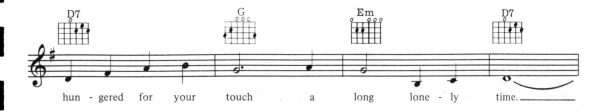

hun - gered for your touch a long lone - ly time. ___

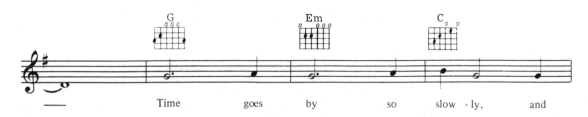

___ Time goes by so slow - ly, and

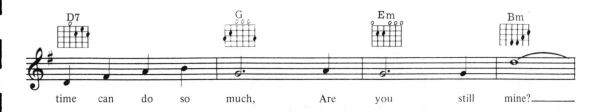

time can do so much, Are you still mine? ___

___ I need your love, ___ I need your love, ___

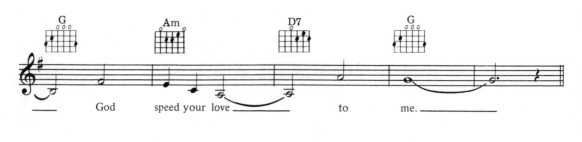

God speed your love _____ to me. _____

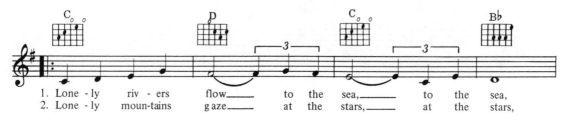

1. Lone - ly riv - ers flow_____ to the sea,_____ to the sea,
2. Lone - ly moun-tains gaze_____ at the stars,_____ at the stars,

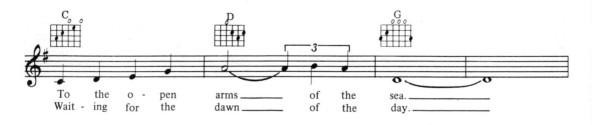

To the o - pen arms _____ of the sea. _____
Wait - ing for the dawn_____ of the day. _____

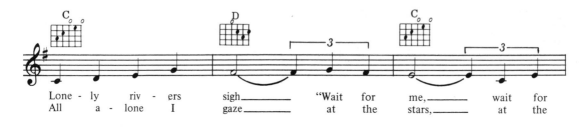

Lone - ly riv - ers sigh_____ "Wait for me,_____ wait for
All a - lone I gaze_____ at the stars,_____ at the

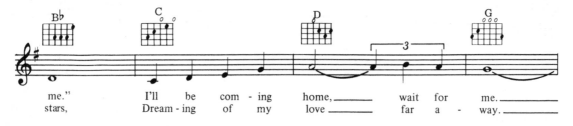

me." I'll be com - ing home,_____ wait for me. _____
stars, Dream - ing of my love _____ far a - way. _____

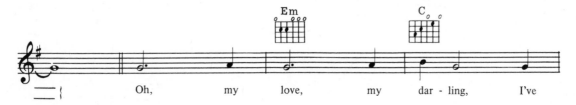

Oh, my love, my dar - ling, I've

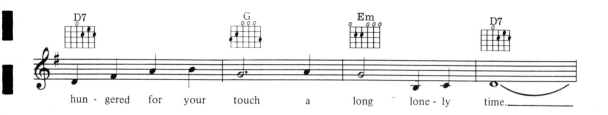

hun - gered for your touch a long lone - ly time._____

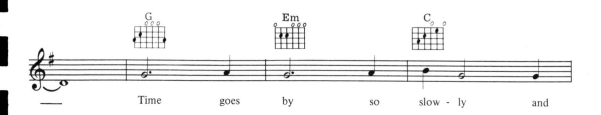

_____ Time goes by so slow - ly and

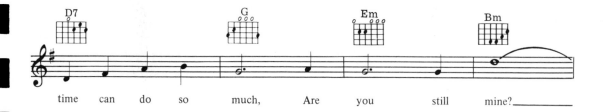

time can do so much, Are you still mine?_____

_____ I need your love,_____ I need your love._____

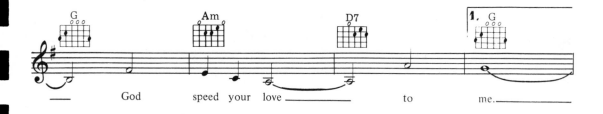

_____ God speed your love _____ to me._____

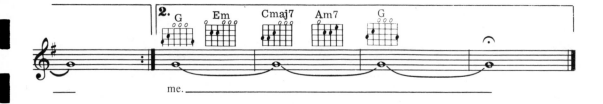

_____ me._____

89
Too Soon To Know

Words & Music by Don Gibson.

Moderato

It's too soon____ to know____ if I can____ for-

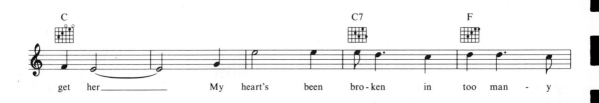

get her____ My heart's been bro-ken in too man-y

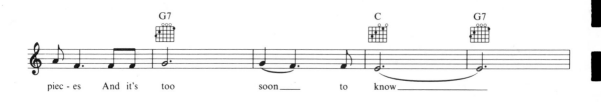

piec-es And it's too soon____ to know____

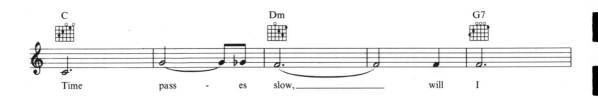

Time pass-es slow,____ will I

ev-er know____ If I can for-get her and

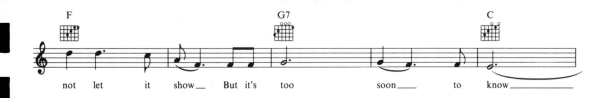

not let it show___ But it's too soon___ to know___

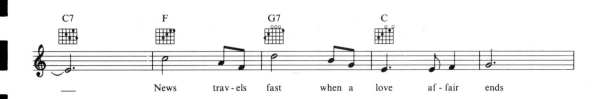

___ News trav-els fast when a love af-fair ends

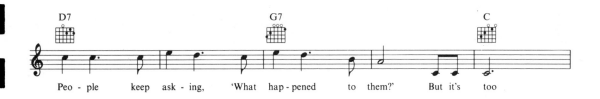

Peo-ple keep ask-ing, 'What hap-pened to them?' But it's too

soon___ to know___ if I can___ for-get her___

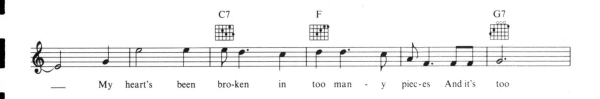

___ My heart's been bro-ken in too man-y piec-es And it's too

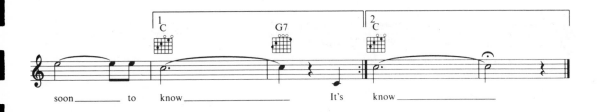

soon___ to know___ It's know___

90
Vincent

Words & Music by Don McLean.

Moderato

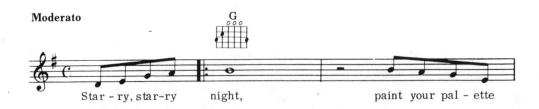

Star - ry, star-ry   night,   paint your pal - ette

blue and grey,   Look out   on   a   summer's day,   with

eyes that know the darkness in   my   soul. Shad-ows on the   hills,

sketch the trees and the   daf - fo - dils,   Catch the breeze and the

win-ter chills, In   col-ours on the snow-y li-nen land.   And now I un-der-

stand   what you tried to   say   to me,   How you suf-fered for your

san -i - ty,   How you tried to set them free. They would not lis-ten, they did

not know how, —   Perhaps they'll listen   now . For they could not   love you,

But still your love was   true,   And when   no   hope   was left   in sight   on that

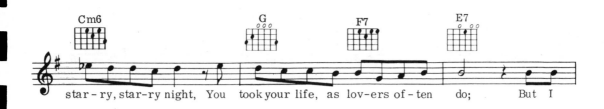

star - ry, star-ry night, You   took your life, as lov-ers of - ten   do;   But I

could have told you, Vin-cent, This world was never meant for one as   beau-ti-ful as   you.

91
Wake Up Little Susie

Words & Music by Felice & Boudleaux Bryant.

— when they say, "Ooh la la" Wake up, — lit - tle Su - sie —

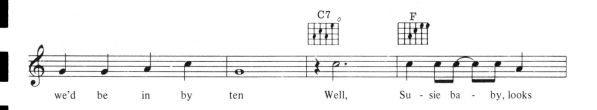

Wake up, — lit - tle Su - sie. _____ Well, we told your Ma - ma that

we'd be in by ten Well, Su - sie ba - by, looks

like we goofed a - gain. ____ Wake up, — lit - tle Su - sie — Wake up, — lit - tle

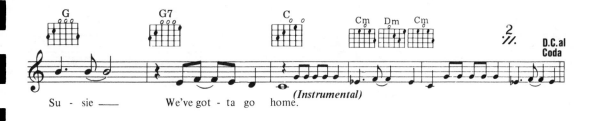

Su - sie ____ We've got - ta go home. *(Instrumental)*

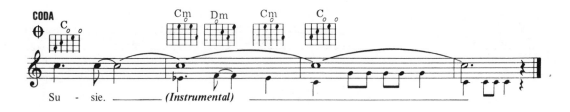

Su - sie. ____ *(Instrumental)* _____

92
The Waltons

By Jerry Goldsmith.

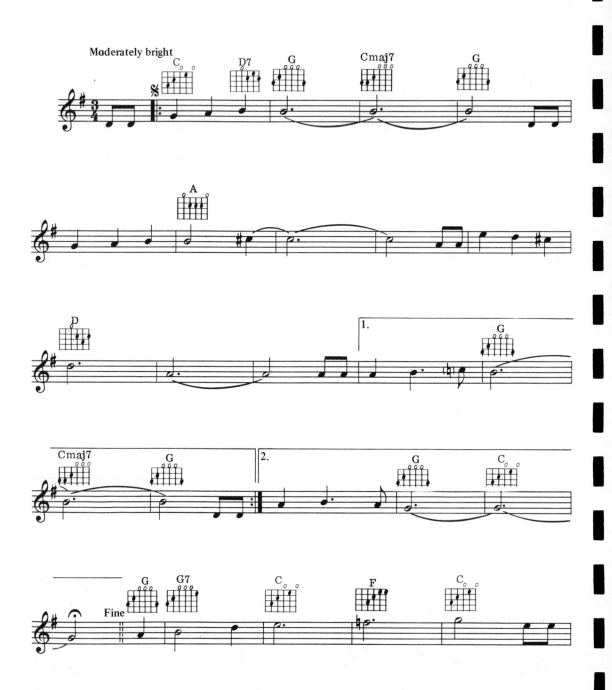

93
We'll Be Together Again

Words by Frankie Laine. Music by Carl Fischer.

Slowly
VERSE ad lib.

Here in our mo-ment of dark-ness, ___ Re-mem-ber the sun has shone;

Laugh and the world will laugh with you, Cry, and you cry a-lone.

A tempo
CHORUS

No tears, no fears, ___ Re-mem-ber there's al-ways to-

mor-row, ___ So what if we have to part, We'll be to-geth-er a-

gain. Your kiss your smile ___. Are mem'ries I'll treas-ure for-

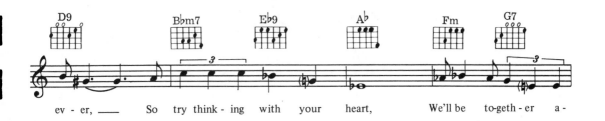

ev - er, ____ So try think - ing with your heart, We'll be to-geth - er a -

gain. Times when I know you'll be lone-some, ____ Times when I know you'll be

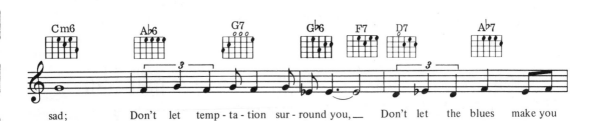

sad; Don't let temp - ta - tion sur - round you, ____ Don't let the blues make you

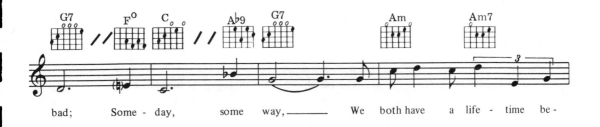

bad; Some - day, some way, _____ We both have a life - time be -

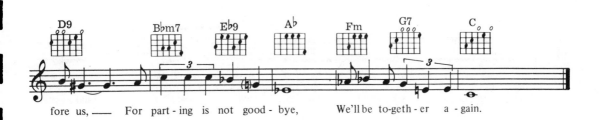

fore us, ____ For part - ing is not good - bye, We'll be to-geth - er a - gain.

94
We Will

Words & Music by Ray O'Sullivan.

Moderato

It's o-ver now you've had ___ your fun ___ get
af-ter-noon we spent ___ the day ___ with
Sun-day next if the wea-ther holds___ we'll

up the stairs ___ go on___quick-ly don't run ___ take off ___ your shoes___
un-cle Frank and his ___ wife aun-tie May___ well do ___ you know___ since then I've re-
have that game ___ but I ___ bags-ie being in goal__ not be-cause I'm good, ___ or be-cause I

both of you's leave ___ them both out-side ___ the door ___ turn the
ceived them be-fore let-ters all ___ of which__ re-peat ___ the same ___ they say
think I should, it's just that well at my age I think stand-ing still _____ would real-ly

land-ing light ___ off, no, wait, leave it on ___ it might make the night___ that much
Thrilled to bits ___ can't be-lieve you came___ we re-lived it both___ o-ver
suit me best___ do we all a-gree?___ hands up those who do___ hands up

eas-ier to be gone and ___ in the morn-ing who'll be wide a-
time and time a-gain and ___ if there's ev-er a chance of e-ven
those who don't I see well in that case will we please be kind en-

95
Wheels

Words by Norman Petty.
Music by Jimmy Torres & Richard Stephens.

Moderato

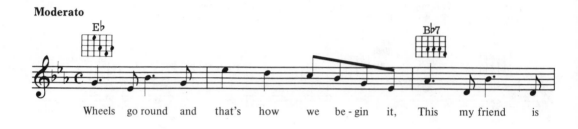

Wheels go round and that's how we be - gin it, This my friend is

love, And now you're in it! Wheels go round, A - round a mile a min - ute,

Fun-ny lit - tle Wheels in - side your heart. Till it's done, There'll

be no way o' know- in', Where you'll run or why you're all a - glow - in',

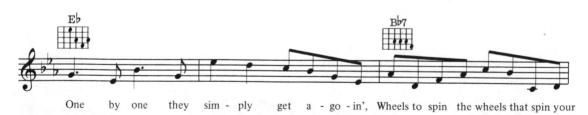

One by one they sim - ply get a - go - in', Wheels to spin the wheels that spin your

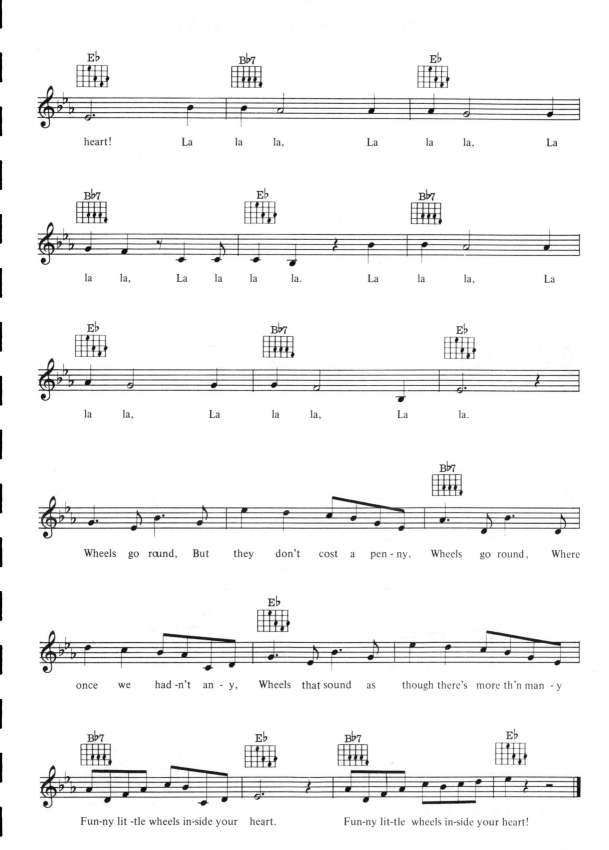

96
When You Ask About Love

Words & Music by Sonny Curtis & Jerry Allison.

Moderato

Don't cry on my shoul-der, re - ly on

some-one who's old-er, I don't know what to tell you when you ask a-bout

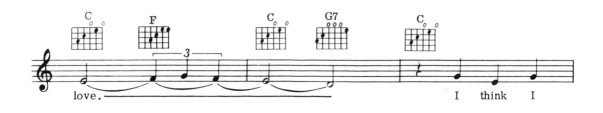

love. _____ I think I

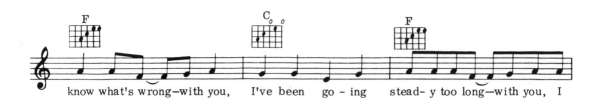

know what's wrong—with you, I've been go - ing stead- y too long—with you, I

don't know what to tell you when you ask a-bout love. _____

What you feel for me is in - fat - u - a - tion and it

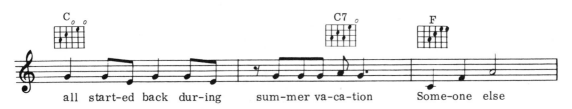

all start-ed back dur-ing sum-mer va-ca-tion Some-one else

needs my at-ten - tion and I can't go stead-y with you no more ——

Don't cry on my should- er, re - ly on

some-one who's old - er, I don't know what to tell you when you ask a-bout

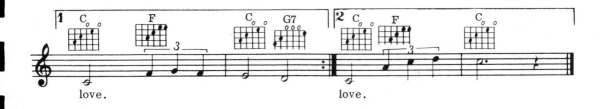

love.   love.

97
Wired For Sound

Words & Music by B.A. Robertson & Alan Tarney.

small speak - ers, I ___ like tall speak - ers. If ___ they've
small boy __ who don't __ like his toys __ I could __ not

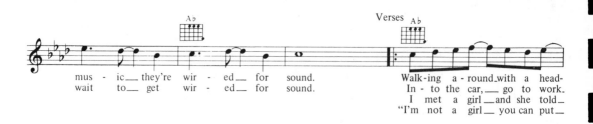

mus - ic __ they're wir - ed __ for sound. Walk-ing a - round __ with a head-
wait to __ get wir - ed __ for sound. In - to the car, __ go to work.
I met a girl __ and she told __
"I'm not a girl __ you can put __

___ ful of mu - sic, cas - sette in my pock - et, and I'm __ gon - na use __ it
___ and I'm cruis - in' I nev - er think __ that I'll blow __ all my fus - es
___ me she loved __ me, I said you love __ me, then love __ means you must __ like
___ on a stand - by, I am a girl __ who de - mands __ that her love __ is

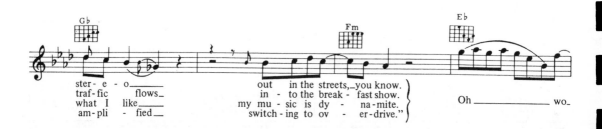

ster - e - o ___ out in the streets, __ you know.
traf - fic flows __ in - to the break - fast show.
what I like ___ my mu - sic is dy - na - mite.
am - pli - fied ___ switch - ing to ov - er - drive."

Oh _____ wo_

98
With A Girl Like You

Words & Music by Reg Presley.

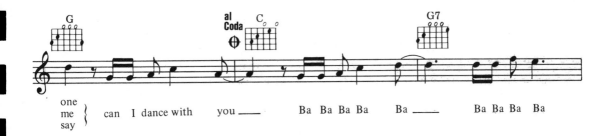

one
me } can I dance with you ___ Ba Ba Ba Ba Ba ___ Ba Ba Ba Ba
say

Ba Ba Ba Ba Ba ___ Ba Ba Ba Ba. I ___ Ba Ba Ba Ba

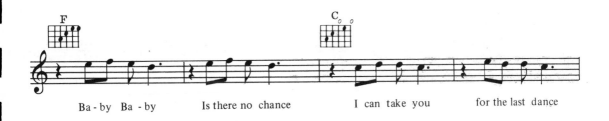

Ba-by Ba-by Is there no chance I can take you for the last dance

all night long yeah I've been wait-ing now there'll be no

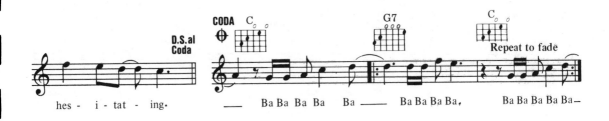

hes-i-tat-ing. ___ Ba Ba Ba Ba Ba ___ Ba Ba Ba Ba, Ba Ba Ba Ba Ba ___

99
You Make Me Feel (Mighty Real)

Words & Music by S. James & J. Wirrick.

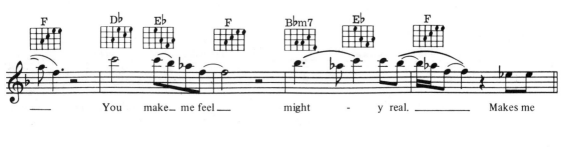

You make me feel mighty real. Makes me

feel might-y real, makes me feel might-y real.

(Instrumental)

You make me feel might-y real.

D.S. to Fade on Chorus

You make me feel might-y real. (3) Well you've

VERSES 2 & 3:

Well you've got me going like I knew you would
And the music's in me and I'm real real hot
And you kiss me there and it feels real good.
'Cause I know you'll love me like you should

100
A Woman In Love

Words & Music by Barry Gibb & Robin Gibb.

Life is a mo-ment in space,——— when the dream is gone———
With you e - ter-nal - ly mine,——— in— love there is———

——— it's a lone - li - er place.
——— no — mea - sure of time.———

I kiss the morn-ing good-bye,——— but down in - side———
We planned it all at the start,——— that you and I———

——— you know we nev - er know why.
——— live in each oth - er's heart.

The road is nar - row and long——— when eyes meet eyes———
We may be o - ceans a - way,——— you feel my love,———

——— and the feel - ing is strong.
I — hear what you say.———

I turn a - way from the wall.——— I stum - ble and fall,———
The truth is nev - er a lie.——— I stum - ble and fall,———

101
You Win Again

Words & Music by Barry Gibb, Robin Gibb & Maurice Gibb.

I couldn't fig-ure why you couldn't give me what ev-'ry-bo-dy needs,—

—— Should-n't let you kick me when I'm

down, my ba — by. Find out

ev-'ry-bo-dy knows that you've been us-in' me,——

I'm sur-prised you will let me stay a-round you.

One day I'm gon-na lift the cov-er and look in-side your heart,——

—— We got a lev-el be-fore we go —— and

Hundreds More Hits For Buskers!

All the songs people love to hear - and sing.

More than a dozen books of all-time hits (with great new titles being added all the time) ...

Including
Ain't No Sunshine
Can't Buy Me Love
Daniel
Ebb Tide
Downtown
English Country Garden
Goodbye Yellow Brick Road
Hey Little Girl
Jailhouse Rock
Laura
Mambo Jumbo
On A Slow Boat To China
Peanut Vendor
Rich Man
Singing In The Rain
Trains And Boats And Planes
Wave
Where Have All The Flowers Gone
and many, many more.

101 Hits for Buskers,
Book 3
Piano/Organ/Guitar
AM25099

101 Hits for Buskers,
Book 4
Piano/Organ/Guitar
AM26550

Piano/Organ Edition with Guitar Chords
Includes:
America
'A' You're Adorable
Can't Give You Anything (But My Love)
Everything From For You
Hands Across The Table
Here Comes Santa Claus
I Feel Pretty
Itsy Bitsy, Teeny Weeny,
Yellow Polkadot Bikini
Just An Old Fashioned Girl
Lambeth Walk
Manana (Is Good Enough For Me)
Maria
The More We Are Together
No Ma Is The Saddest Word
Pretty Little Black Eyed Susie
The Rhythm Of Life
Somewhere
Swedish Rhapsody (Midsummer Vigil)
Tonight!
Walk On The Wild Side
Waltz Time
When The Lights Go On Again
(All Over The World)
You Are Beautiful!
and many, many more.

101 Hits for Buskers,
Book 12
Piano/Organ/Guitar
AM79765

101 Hits for Buskers,
Book 2
Piano/Organ/Guitar
AM19803

101 Hits for Buskers,
Book 2
Bb Edition
AM19811

Arranged for Piano/Organ with Guitar Chords, includes:
Always There
Born In The USA
Brothers In Arms
Every Loser Wins
How Will I Know
I Want To Wake Up With You
Memory
Only Love
Separate Lives
Sweet Freedom
The Lady In Red
The Sun Always Shines On TV
The Way It Is
Walking In The Air (Theme from 'The Snowman')
(What A) Wonderful World
What's Love Got To Do With It
When The Going Gets Tough, The Tough Get Going
Who's Zoomin' Who?
You Can Call Me Al
and many, many more.

101 Hits for Buskers,
Book 11
Piano/Organ/Guitar
AM77306

101 Hits for Buskers,
Book 13
Piano/Organ/Guitar
AM84062

101 Hits for Buskers,
Book 1
Piano/Organ/Guitar
AM 17229

INCLUDES
ALL SHOOK UP
BRIDGE OVER TROUBLED WATER
DON'T GO BREAKING MY HEART
EVERGREEN
THE GIRL FROM IPANEMA
HAIR
IMAGINE
JUST THE TWO OF US
LADY
LIGHT MY FIRE
MISS YOU NIGHTS
NOBODY DOES IT BETTER
RIVERS OF BABYLON
SEE YOU LATER ALLIGATOR
STARTING OVER
THIS OLE HOUSE
THE WINNER TAKES IT ALL
THE WONDER OF YOU
YOU NEVER DONE IT LIKE THAT
AND MANY, MANY MORE

101 Hits for Buskers,
Book 9
Piano/Organ/Guitar
AM66366

Piano/Organ Edition with Guitar Chords
A Taste Of Honey
Caravan
Fire And Rain
If I Can Help Somebody
Jezebel
Kisses Sweeter Than Wine
Love Me With All Your Heart
Moonlight And Roses
Nancy (With The Laughing Face)
Only You
Poor People Of Paris, The
Rainy Days And Mondays
Rockin' Chair
Song From Moulin Rouge, The
Something Is Happening
Swingin' Shepherd Blues
Together
That's My Weakness Now
Take A Chance On Me
Watch What Happens
Without Her
When You Wish Upon A Star
Yesterday Once More
and many, many more.

101 Hits for Buskers,
Book 10
Piano/Organ/Guitar
AM66440

101 HITS FOR BUSKERS
BOOK 5 PIANO/ORGAN EDITION WITH GUITAR CHORDS

101 Hits for Buskers,
Book 7
Piano/Organ/Guitar
AM33654

101 Hits for Buskers,
Book 8
Piano/Organ/Guitar
AM36914

101 Hits for Buskers
Book 10 Piano/Organ Edition with Guitar Chords

101 Hits for Buskers,
Book 5
Piano/Organ/Guitar
AM29570

101 Hits for Buskers,
Book 6
Piano/Organ/Guitar
AM29869

101 Hits for Buskers
Book 6 Piano/Organ Edition with Guitar Chords
Includes
Climb Ev'ry Mountain
Don't Cry For Me Argentina
Edelweiss
Happy Talk
Hello, Young Lovers
It Must Be Love
Mull Of Kintyre
People Will Say We're In Love
Scarborough Fair
Silly Love Songs
Some Enchanted Evening
Somewhere In The Night
The Sound Of Music
What A Wonderful World
With You I'm Born Again
Younger Than Springtime
and many, many more.

Available from all good music shops.

In case of difficulty, please contact:
Music Sales Limited
Newmarket Road, Bury St Edmunds,
Suffolk IP33 3YB.
Telephone: 0284 702600.

Bringing you the world's best music.

Plus many indispensable collections of special interest:
101 Jazz & Blues Hits ...
101 Showtunes ...
101 Beatles Songs ...
101 Pub Favourites ...
and more.

Busking For Special Occasions 101 Songs:
Piano/Organ/Guitar
AM29596

101 Rock'n'Roll Hits for Buskers
Piano/Organ/Guitar
AM36484

101 Pub Favourites for Buskers
Piano/Organ/Guitar
AM62761

101 Christmas Hits for Buskers
Piano/Organ/Guitar
AM64569

101 Australian Songs For Buskers
Piano/Organ/Guitar
AM68073

101 Beatles Songs for Buskers
Piano/Organ/Guitar
N018392

101 Country Hits for Buskers
Piano/Organ/Guitar
AM33580

101 Jazz & Blues Hits for Buskers
Piano/Organ/Guitar
AM60245

101 Stage & Screen Hits For Buskers
Piano/Organ/Guitar
AM72612

101 Australian Songs For Buskers, Book 2
Piano/Keyboard/Guitar
AM78684

101 Folk Songs for Buskers
Piano/Organ/Guitar
AM69220

101 Comedy Hits for Buskers
Piano/Organ/Guitar
AM37912

101 Children's Songs For Buskers
Piano/Organ/Guitar
AM74584

101 Showtunes For Buskers
Piano/Organ/Guitar
AM32509

101 Classical Themes For Buskers
Piano/Organ/Guitar
AM65319

101 Pop Hits for Buskers
Piano/Organ/Guitar
AM61763

101 Rock Hits for Buskers
AM65806

101 Rock Hits for Buskers, Book 2
AM84716